MEN AND VOLTS AT WAR

The Story of the General Electric Company in World War II

by John Anderson Miller

The story of how the largest electrical manufacturing company mobilized all its experience, skill, and resourcefulness for America's war effort is one that needed to be told. It is a story of hard work and long hours, but it is also a story full of drama, excitement, and romance— a dynamic pattern woven by human hands and brains, fired by enthusiasm and tempered by organization.

War has always been a grim drama of men and materials. In the early part of World War II, the United Nations were short of both, and the Axis Powers came close to domination of the world. But when American manpower and the productive capacity of American industry were mobilized, the forces of the United Nations became irresistible, and nothing could halt their victorious progress.

Most important was the fighting spirit of the men of the armed forces. But equipment was essential, too. In

(Continued on back flap)

(Continued from front flap)

reaching a production three times its normal peacetime volume, American industry exceeded all expectations. New plants had to be built, and people had to be taught to use new techniques. New and fantastic tools and machines of attack and defense were designed, and plans had to be changed as battles taught new lessons. It was an accomplishment exceeding any similar effort of man.

This production war was fought by large and small factories from coast to coast. Every unit in American industry shared in the effort. Upon some industries and companies, however, there fell an exceptionally heavy burden of responsibility; by nature of the business in which they were engaged, they alone had the experience and facilities required to make certain essential equipment and to make it quickly in large quantities.

It is probable that General Electric produced a greater variety of complex war equipment and was called upon to solve a greater variety of difficult technical problems than any other manufacturer. This is the story of G-E's accomplishments in World War II, and it represents the work of more than 175,000 of the men and women who battled for everything for which America stands by making the things which were absolutely essential for victory.

Men and Volts at War

". . . in memory of 1055 men and women of this organization who gave their lives in the service of their country in World War II."

★ ★ ★

More than 50,000 men and women of General Electric served in the armed forces during the war. This book is not their story; their accomplishment is written in the larger book of history.

This volume is the story of the men and women who stayed at home, who, although they could not *win* the war, could—through failure to do their part—help to *lose* it. How they met that challenge is the story of Men and Volts at War.

MEN *and* VOLTS
AT WAR

The Story of General Electric
in World War II

by

John Anderson Miller

Author of
Master Builders of Sixty Centuries
Fares Please!

54811

Whittlesey House

McGRAW-HILL BOOK COMPANY, INC.

NEW YORK : LONDON

MEN AND VOLTS AT WAR

COPYRIGHT, 1947, BY
GENERAL ELECTRIC COMPANY

*The quality of the materials used in the manufacture of
this book is governed by continued postwar shortages.*

PUBLISHED BY WHITTLESEY HOUSE

a division of the McGraw-Hill Book Company, Inc.

PRINTED IN THE UNITED STATES OF AMERICA
BY THE KINGSPORT PRESS, INC.

Foreword

War has always been a grim drama of men and materials. In the early part of World War II, the United Nations were short of both, and the Axis Powers came close to domination of the world. But when American manpower and the productive capacity of American industry were mobilized, the forces of the United Nations became irresistible, and nothing could halt their victorious progress.

Most important was the indomitable fighting spirit of the men of the armed forces. But equipment was essential, too. "To the civilian workers of factory and farm," said General Eisenhower in his report on the operations in Europe, "we are forever indebted. Our enormous material superiority gave us an unchallengeable advantage over our foes. No army or navy was ever supported so generously or so well."

In reaching a production three times its normal peacetime volume, American industry exceeded all expectations. New plants had to be built and people had to be taught to use new techniques. New and fantastic tools and machines of attack and defense were designed, and plans had to be changed as battles taught new lessons. It was an accomplishment exceeding any similar effort of man.

This production war was fought by large and small factories from coast to coast. Every unit in American industry shared in the effort. Upon some industries and companies, however, there fell an exceptionally heavy burden of responsibility; by nature of the business in which they were engaged, they alone had the experience and facilities required to make certain essential equipment, and to make it quickly in large quantities.

One of these companies was General Electric. During an inspection tour of the company's Syracuse plant, Secretary of the Navy, Frank Knox, made the statement:

No single industry in America has made a better response, a quicker response, to our appeal for help than General Electric. I don't think what you've done here can be duplicated anywhere in the world. And it's that quality of America that makes it possible to get into this war late and unprepared, and within a year, so affect its complexion as to change the whole posture of the Allies from one of defense to one of growing offense. You are making the things which are absolutely essential to victory in this war, so lift up your heads with pride—the same kind of pride that men who wear the uniforms of this country have when they go forth to do battle for us—because in the truest possible sense you are battling for everything for which America stands.

The story of how the largest electrical manufacturing company mobilized all its experience, skill, and resourcefulness for America's war effort on land, at sea, and in the air is one that needed to be told. With the end of hostilities, then, the war records of General Electric and its associated companies were made available to Mr. Miller. At the same time he was able to talk with those who guided the policies of the company during that period, with the scientists and engineers who were designing the equipments, and with the workers in shops and offices.

General Electric's accomplishments represented the work of more than 175,000 men and women. Many were singled out for special commendation by the Army, Navy, and other government agencies. Many others worked with equal skill and devotion under circumstances that precluded individual recognition. Since it would be impossible to mention all to whom credit is due, this story of the company's war work has necessarily been written without emphasis on the contributions of particular individuals.

Altogether, it is probable that General Electric produced

a greater variety of complex war equipment and was called upon to solve a greater variety of difficult technical problems than any other manufacturer. It is a story of hard work and long hours, but it is also a story full of drama, excitement, and romance—a dynamic pattern woven by human hands and brains, fired by enthusiasm and tempered by organization.

CHARLES E. WILSON.

Contents

1

It Was an Electric War

HEAVY SEAS WERE BREAKING over the bows of the U.S.S. *South Dakota* and her sister ship the U.S.S. *Washington* as they plowed through the waters off Guadalcanal on a dark November night in 1942. It was the velvet darkness of the tropics—and the ships were hunting the Jap fleet. But they were not hunting by human eye. The invisible searchlight beam of American radar was probing the blackness of the night around them.

Suddenly the beam picked up a Japanese battleship a little more than 8 miles away. The powerful 16-inch rifles were elevated and aimed at the spot where radar said there was a target. The big guns hurled their tons of steel and explosive into the darkness. Seconds later another thundering salvo followed, and the spot disappeared from the radar screen. Before the battle ended the *South Dakota* and the *Washington* had sunk three Japanese cruisers and a battleship, though no American eye had seen them.

That is characteristic of modern warfare. Firing a big gun either at sea or on land is not simply a matter of sighting on the target and pulling the lanyard. Seldom is the target visible to the gunner. Such factors as wind direction and velocity, temperature, atmospheric density, and even the rota-

1

tion of the earth must be taken into account. More than twenty different operations are involved in bringing a big gun to bear on its target, and all of them must be performed with speed and precision.

EVOLUTION OF FIGHTING METHODS

From the time of Caesar to the early years of the twentieth century, success in war depended largely on the personal prowess of the individual fighter. More recently physical strength has become less important, though courage, as always, is the first essential. World War I was in considerable measure a mechanical war—to some extent a war on wheels. But World War II was largely an electrical war. On land, at sea, and in the air, examples of the use of electricity were found everywhere.

When landing craft had carried troops and equipment to the shore in North Africa, Sicily, France, and the islands of the Pacific, the bow doors were opened and the ramps lowered by electric motors. The famous M-4 tanks that paced the drive of the American Army from the beaches of Normandy to the banks of the Rhine each carried electric-generating equipment to produce about as much current as is used by the ordinary home. Engineers employed thousands of miles of copper wire for detonating explosives by electricity. The buzz bomb met its master in the radar-controlled antiaircraft gun firing shells with electric proximity fuses. The entire army—in tanks and jeeps, in foxholes, at headquarters, and even slogging along on foot—was tied together by radio.

Electricity was the nerve system of every warship. More than 10 per cent of a ship's total cost went for electrical equipment. A big warship often required as much electric power as a city like San Diego, or Omaha, or Syracuse, and for very similar purposes. Huge electric motors turned the propeller shafts. Lamp bulbs had to be kept burning in thousands of sockets. There were electric fans, pumps, compressors, winches, and a hundred other devices. There were electric ranges, fry kettles, griddles, and bake ovens to keep the men at sea well fed, fit, and happy.

Electric equipment was a vital part of the airplane, too. In the Battle of Britain, the Royal Air Force lost 40 of its precious bombers one winter night, principally because the hydraulic-control mechanisms froze in the subzero temperatures. Redesign of the equipment for electric operation began immediately. The B-29 Superfortress, so thoroughly American in the boldness of its conception and the excellence of its design, was electrified throughout. The flight of the plane was electrically controlled by an automatic pilot. Crews were provided with electrically heated clothing. Each plane had 170 electric motors to operate wing flaps, landing gear, bomb doors, turret drive, gun charger, computer, fuel pumps, and other equipment.

"Gadgets," cried one veteran aviator, "have no glamor, but they will probably win this war. Dropping a blockbuster is important, but what good is a blockbuster if you can't get the bomb-bay doors open?"

THE JOB THAT "COULDN'T BE DONE"

President Roosevelt's statement to Congress on May 16, 1940, that the United States must build 50,000 airplanes a year set in motion the greatest armament program ever known. At first his proposal was greeted with astonishment and skepticism—abroad and at home. To a country that had never built one-tenth that number of planes in any previous year, this seemed like asking the impossible. Most people believed in their hearts that it could not be done. Maybe 20,000 planes a year could be built, they thought, but even that would be little short of a miracle.

But American industry rolled up its sleeves and went to work—slowly at first, and then with ever-increasing speed. Other nations had long envied America's ability to mass-produce canned soups, automobiles, electric kitchens, kiddy cars, and whatever could be used in quantity. Enraged by the attack on Pearl Harbor, America showed that it could mass-produce airplanes, tanks, guns, ships, and other material in endless variety.

In the first 12 months after Pearl Harbor, American aircraft manufacturers built 47,836 planes, in 1943 they built 85,898, and in 1944 nearly 100,000. From the middle of 1940 to the end of the war the total was almost 300,000. Moreover, those being built at the end of the war were far larger and heavier than the planes being produced when the war started—averaging 11,000 pounds as against 4,000 pounds.

Airplanes, of course, were only one part of the war program. During the 4½ years between President Roosevelt's message and the end of the war, American industry also turned out 86,333 tanks, 104,891 armored cars and jeeps, 12½ million rifles and carbines, 2,600,000 machine guns, 216,000 artillery pieces, and all the related materiel to equip an army of 8 million men, as well as some 5,000 ships to carry the men and their equipment overseas. A navy of unmatched size and power had been created, too. As late as 1940 the United States Navy had only 383 combat ships. By the end of the war it had some 1,300 such ships, with an aggregate tonnage of more than five times what it had been before the war.

Never was the fundamental strength of the United States so clearly evident as in World War II. In the black days that followed Pearl Harbor, the United States and its allies in the coalition of the United Nations stood close to defeat. But the United Nations had one paramount advantage—the productive capacity of American industry. The job that "couldn't be done" was done.

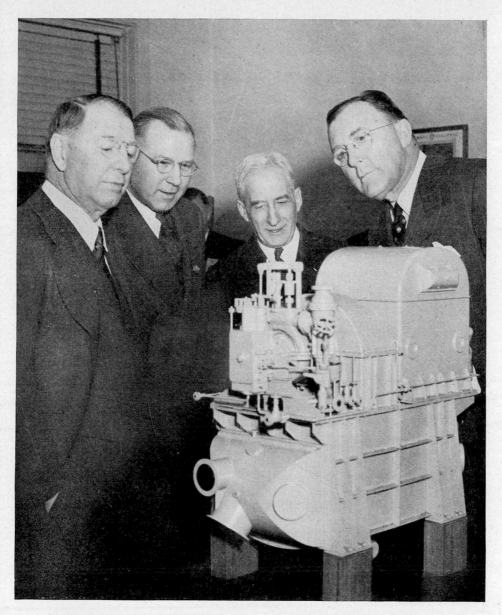

Secretary of the Navy Frank Knox and Charles E. Wilson, Executive Vice Chairman of the United States War Production Board, inspecting model of a destroyer escort turbine at Syracuse. In background Gerard Swope, then President of General Electric, and, on his right, W. E. Saupe, Superintendent of the Syracuse Plant. Mr. Wilson served as President of the company from 1939 to late in 1942 when he resigned to become a member of the War Production Board. After devoting approximately two years to the government's war production program, he returned to the presidency of General Electric in September, 1944.

Philip D. Reed (right) receiving the congratulations of Owen D. Young when Reed resumed his post of Chairman of the Board after serving as Chief of the United States Mission for Economic Affairs, in London. Mr. Reed was originally elected chairman in 1939, but at the end of 1942 resigned to give full time to the service of the government, turning over the chairmanship to former Chairman Young.

General Electric's War Projects Committee, which supervised all the company's far-flung war activities, shown here in 1942 reporting to President Charles E. Wilson. Left to right: J. F. Cunningham; Chester H. Lang, chairman; Mr. Wilson; J. G. Farrar; and H. A. Winne.

COMPLEX WAR-PRODUCTION MACHINE

Because of its character and scope, World War II presented more formidable electrical problems than any previous conflict. But a visitor walking into the offices of the General Electric Company at Schenectady during the war years would have found little to indicate the dynamic nature of the company's participation in the war effort. Except for the armed guards at the gate and the identification badges worn by the employees, everything appeared normal. Actually these offices were the nerve center of one of the world's biggest and most complex war machines.

When the National Defense Program was first announced, the company volunteered to do its share. Then little by little —and more and more—the company was drafted for war work. What began as a part-time job turned into a full-time job with overtime.

That this would inevitably occur was foreseen even before the fall of France. On the day of the German break-through at Sedan, a meeting was in progress at Erie to discuss the company's sales program. At the head of the table sat Chester H. Lang, newly appointed manager of apparatus sales. Suddenly the telephone rang. President Charles E. Wilson was calling Mr. Lang on long distance.

"Chet," he said, "unless I miss my guess, all hell's going to break loose! We've got to have some means of coordinating our efforts and facilities so as to help the government all we can in speeding up this big defense program. I'm appointing a committee for this job—and you're the chairman."

Thus was born the Defense Coordinating Committee, known after Pearl Harbor as the "War Projects Committee," which ultimately held almost daily meetings covering every phase of the company's war activity. In addition to Lang its membership included H. A. Winne, assistant to the vice-president in charge of engineering, J. G. Farrar, assistant comptroller, and J. F. Cunningham, assistant to the vice-president in charge of manufacturing. The magnitude of the committee's task can be measured by the fact that, in the aggregate, General Electric produced about 4 billion dollars of war equipment, ranging from the giant turbines for battleships to delicate instruments for airplanes and mass spectrometers for the atomic bomb project.

MAJOR TASKS UNDERTAKEN

Pound-wise and dollar-wise, G.E.'s biggest war job was building propulsion units to drive the Navy's fighting ships and the vessels of the rapidly growing Merchant Marine. These propulsion units—turbine-generators and motors, and geared turbines—are vital organs of a modern ship.

All the major vessels in the Navy's wartime shipbuilding program were equipped with turbine-gear drive. Hundreds of others had turbine-electric drive. Turbines were supplied by General Electric for 6 of the 10 new battleships, for 37 of the 43 new cruisers, for 10 of the 27 new aircraft carriers, and for 200 of the 364 new destroyers. Gears to match the turbines were made for the bulk of these ships. In addition the company provided turbine-electric drive for 244 destroyer escorts as well as turbine equipment for some 300 naval auxiliary vessels and 800 ships for the Merchant Marine. It was entrusted with the production of 60 per cent of the electric drive for the wartime submarine fleet. Altogether, three-fourths of the Navy's total propulsion and auxiliary turbine horsepower built during the war period was produced by G.E. or built by others to G-E design.

For warfare in the air, too, the company's production was on a stupendous scale. In the spring of 1940 a power-operated turret was high on the "must" list of the Army Air Forces. An electric-drive system developed by the company quickly demonstrated its efficiency. First in quantities of hundreds per week and later in thousands per week the company supplied the motors and control, which were the heart of the power-turret system. This turret program placed a greater load on the company's small motor facilities than any other single project—in war or peace—in the entire history of the company.

Experience in World War I had taught the importance of being on top in the struggle for mastery in the air. Beginning in 1917 the company and the Army Air Forces had worked together to perfect the turbosupercharger—a device to enable planes to fly higher and higher. By the late 1930's the "turbo" was standard equipment on nearly all American high-altitude fighters and bombers. Wartime expansion of the Air Forces caused the demand for this device to skyrocket. Whole factories were devoted to its manufacture. In all, the company turned out more than 162,000.

Other major war tasks were the making of electric motors totaling some 300,000 horsepower for landing craft, the design and manufacture of more than 300 new types of wartime lamps, and the production of four times the company's normal volume of electrical control apparatus. General Electric was the first to go into large-scale production of radar equipment for the Navy. Millions of small electric measurement devices were made for radar and radio. The company turned out approximately 400,000 electrically heated suits for fliers. It also made such apparatus as howitzers, fuses, "bazookas," searchlights, naval gun directors and mounts, and a formidable array of other things.

PRECISION IN MANUFACTURE

These figures are impressive, but war production was far more than a matter of quantity. Equipment provided for the Army and the Navy had to be good—better than the corresponding equipment possessed by the enemy. And it was. "The superiority of American armament, both quantitatively and qualitatively, was so great," said Gen. George C.

Marshall, Chief of Staff of the United States Army, "that we dared to mount operations all over the world with a strategic inferiority in numbers of troops."

Skillful design and expert workmanship were required to produce the superior quality of American equipment. Consider ship turbines. Steam enters a turbine at a pressure of 700 pounds per square inch and a velocity many times that of a tropical hurricane. It emerges a fraction of a second later at less than atmospheric pressure. The turbine wheels turn at 10,000 revolutions per minute, their outer edges traveling 600 miles an hour. To build one of these big turbines involves the use of about 700 working drawings and the services of more than 4,000 skilled engineers and workmen.

To harness a turbine to the propeller shaft requires gears which may be as large as 200 inches in diameter and which may weigh 70,000 pounds. Tooth spacing in these gears, however, must not vary more than three-tenths of a mil, which is about one-fourth the thickness of a cigarette paper.

This watchmaker's precision in the manufacture of propulsion machinery gave American warships unmatched reliability of performance. In 3 years of combat service the U.S.S. *North Carolina* sailed more than 250,000 nautical miles, or ten times the distance around the earth. She was part of the bombardment force in five major Pacific campaigns, successfully beat off more than a score of enemy air attacks, and was still triumphantly afloat at the war's end. "The impressive combat record of this ship," said Rear Admiral E. L. Cochrane, Chief of the Bureau of Ships, "would have been impossible without the reliable performance contributed by her General Electric propulsion machinery."

STURDY CONSTRUCTION

With electricity used for a wide variety of purposes on shipboard, there is need for a great quantity of indicating and control apparatus. A large ship may require as many as 2,000 individual electric meters, instruments, and control devices. Before the war both the British and the United States Navies considered the electric equipment on their ships about all that could be desired. But when the British clashed with German bombs and mines, they found that direct hits and near misses frequently put the control systems out of use in ways and under circumstances that threatened disaster.

Observing this, the U.S. Navy hurriedly called on General Electric for complete new lines of shockproof meters and controls. Equipment developed as a result of this urgent appeal proved to be so different from that previously in use that extensive revisions were necessary in manufacturing methods and facilities. These changes, coupled with the need for greater volume and faster deliveries than at any previous time in history, posed design problems of the first magnitude.

Delivery of the first of the new meters and controls was made within a few months after Pearl Harbor. Others followed rapidly. By the time of the big naval battles that accompanied the landings on Leyte and Okinawa, a large amount of the new equipment had been installed on the ships of the fleet. Again and again it proved its worth. Near misses and direct hits shook the ships from stem to stern, but they continued to function unhampered by difficulties with the electric controls.

INTRICACIES OF DESIGN

Warfare in the air presented many intricate design problems, too. For example, remote-control equipment for aircraft gun turrets was in full production when a query came from the Army Air Forces; could the company also design and build a computer to perform quickly and accurately the complicated calculations involved in aiming these guns? Firing a stationary gun at a stationary target is a relatively simple matter. Firing from a plane traveling at 300 or 400 miles an hour at another plane traveling at the same speed necessitates that the gun be so aimed that the projectile will meet the target and not pass ahead or behind, above or below it. The speeds and directions of both planes, the distance between them, the effect of the wind, and several more factors must be taken into consideration—and all this elaborate calculation must be done in the twinkling of an eye.

To design and build computers on a schedule that would catch up with airplane production seemed impossible. Previous experience in building computers for use on shipboard had shown that 2 or 3 years were ordinarily necessary to do the job. An air-borne computer was altogether new. To provide computing equipment that could be flown involved a weight reduction to about one-tenth of the surface-ship standard. Moreover, the equipment had to be designed for high production instead of the low production customarily associated with naval computers.

Computers are closely integrated devices with a high degree of interdependence between the various elements. A small group of engineers and draftsmen can usually handle the designing job most effectively. But this job could not wait for that, so a new "unit design" technique was evolved. A basic design was worked out, composed of seventeen subassemblies that could be designed independently and fitted together when completed. Teams of engineers and draftsmen were assigned to work out the details of the various units. In this way more than 1,000 detailed drawings were turned out in 4½ months, and a finished computer was in operation in 6½ months from the time of the original inquiry.

Manufacture of the computers involved the making of component parts tooled to tolerances of not more than one ten-thousandth of an inch. Assembly of these parts required technical proficiency of a high order. These jobs were given to the Lamp Department whose workers were thoroughly accustomed to precision manufacture. Some 2,000 skilled workers were kept busy on this assignment, three shifts a day, throughout the war.

PRODUCTIVE "KNOW-HOW"

All along the line the story was the same. The war-production job was one of prodigious quantities of all kinds of equipment. But it was also a job of constantly seeking ways to improve that equipment. Only the best was good enough, and the best of today might be second best next week.

At the beginning of the war the Axis powers had an overwhelming advantage in equipment, resulting from years of experimentation and preparation. Yet their advance preparation was no match for the productive "know-how" of American industry. The early succession of impressive Axis victories came to an inglorious end when they faced the best equipped armies and fleets the world had ever seen.

2

Horsepower Afloat

WHEN AMERICA FOUND HERSELF AT WAR, she determined to build the most powerful navy ever known. Resolutely President Roosevelt announced, "We shall carry the attack against the enemy—we shall hit him and hit him again wherever and whenever we can reach him." In line with this, the Navy disclosed that U.S. warships could go farther and hit harder because they consumed from 25 to 40 per cent less fuel than the ships of other nations. Their turbine-propulsion equipment was more powerful, more efficient, weighed less, and was more dependable than any other ship-propulsion machinery in the world.

TURBINES FOR SHIP PROPULSION

Development of the Navy's turbine drive was no overnight miracle. Its beginnings went back more than 40 years to the time when the General Electric Company installed a system of electric motors and control for operating gun turrets on the cruiser *Brooklyn*. This installation was in the nature of an experiment. A year or two earlier General Electric had equipped one cruiser and three battleships with motors for operating ammunition hoists. But at that time many naval authorities had grave doubts about the superiority of electric turret operation over the steam operation then in general use. Despite this skepticism, the company had firm faith in the idea and offered to stand the cost of the experiment if it should fail. Another who had faith was the then Lt. Bradley A. Fiske, later to become one of America's most famous admirals. Hilary A. Herbert, at that time Secretary of the Navy, was willing to try the experiment on the proposed basis and gave permission to go ahead.

The tests of the turret-operating mechanism on the *Brooklyn* were a tremendous success. "No triumph could have been more complete," said Lieutenant Fiske in writing of the experiment. It marked the beginning of the extensive use of electric apparatus on naval vessels. From that time onward, electricity played an increasingly important part in the operation of American fighting ships.

In 1909, W. L. R. Emmet, a General Electric engineer world famous for his work on steam turbines and electric-generating machinery, proposed the use of electric drive for large naval ships. His idea was to generate the power by means of turbine-generators and to drive the propellers by means of powerful electric motors. Such an arrangement would be a great improvement, he believed, over the use of reciprocating steam engines. The turbine, operating at high speed with high-pressure steam, produced far more power in proportion to the weight of the machinery and required less fuel. Use of electric generators and motors to step down the rapid rotation of the turbine to the relatively slow rotation of the propeller introduced certain complications and extra weight, but there was no alternative because no way was known to construct speed-reducing gears of large enough size and of sufficient strength to drive a large vessel.

EXPERIMENT WITH THE *JUPITER*

Emmet's idea was to try out the turbine-electric-drive system on a battleship, but the Navy thought that would be too risky. Agreement was reached, however, to make the trial on a collier. The *Jupiter*, one of the three new colliers then under construction, was selected for the experiment.

She was put in commission in 1913, and her trial runs were anxiously watched. Unless this radically new method of ship propulsion proved its superiority beyond question, the Navy Department could not consider substituting it for the well-established system of ship propulsion. Fortunately, the tests were conclusive. Turbine-electric propulsion was as completely successful as the turret drives had been on the *Brooklyn*.

On the basis of experience with the *Jupiter*, the Navy changed its plans for the propulsion equipment for the battleship *New Mexico*, then being built. In 1917 this 32,000-ton vessel was launched with the most powerful electrical machinery ever installed in any vessel up to that time. Again electricity proved its worth, and a number of other capital ships were similarly equipped.

BUILDING THE NEW NAVY

Then came the long naval holiday when no new ships were laid down. In the early 1930's, however, the Navy decided to build a number of new destroyers and wanted the most up-to-date possible propulsion machinery for them. By this time the art of gear making had been advanced to a point where gears could be designed for loads tremendously greater than the maximum loads of a few years before. So General Electric proposed for the new destroyers a geared turbine drive utilizing a compact, high-pressure high-speed steam turbine, geared directly to the propeller shaft. This idea was approved by the Navy, and the first vessel so equipped, the U.S.S. *Mahan*, went into service in 1936. She showed a decrease in fuel consumption of about 25 per cent, and represented, according to Charles Edison, then Secretary of the Navy, the greatest progress the Navy had made in engineering in a generation.

Development of this type of propulsion came at a fortunate time. It set the style for the new Navy that the United States was just starting to build. The great battleships *North Carolina, Washington, South Dakota, Massachusetts, Iowa,* and *Missouri,* the fast new cruisers and carriers, and the host of scurrying destroyers all were equipped with geared turbine-propulsion machinery.

The resulting reduction of fuel consumption was an outstanding advantage of this type of equipment. On a certain task force mission during the war the British battleship *King George V* was reported to have required three refuelings to two required by the U.S.S. *Washington.* The British thereupon sent a mission to the United States to study the American propulsion equipment. With the permission of the U.S. Navy the members of this commission visited the Schenectady Works to learn in detail the means by which this remarkable fuel economy was accomplished.

Not only was this machinery efficient, but it was sturdy and dependable in battle. The aircraft carrier *Independence* had one of its two main propellers carried away during an engagement in the Pacific, and both units in its after turbine room flooded. When the battle was over it crossed the Pacific Ocean and came into dock at Hunter's Point, Calif., at 17 knots on its outboard port turbine alone.

In the Navy's never-ending struggle against attack from the air, many a ship was saved by the performance of her propulsion machinery. The story told of the encounter between an American heavy cruiser and a Japanese dive bomber is typical.

On the bridge of the U.S. warship stood the officer of the deck conversing with the navigator. Suddenly came a voice from the near-by speaking tube.

"Jap dive bombers approaching, sir!"

In a moment the bombers were overhead, circling around and around. They were so high that their movements seemed almost lazy and sluggish. Then a wasplike shape separated itself from the group and started to swoop downward. The ship's antiaircraft batteries opened up with a roar. Steel went hurtling skyward to meet the attacker. Bright orange bursts of flack, followed by mushrooming puffs of smoke, filled the sky.

"Jap bomber diving, sir," came the voice from the tube.

The officer waited calmly a few seconds. Then he acted.

"Full speed ahead! Hard left rudder!" he shouted.

With water foaming under her bow the ship began to swing. Her decks were slanting like a destroyer's in a heavy sea. Down came the dive bomber. At 1,500 feet a bomb suddenly separated itself from the onrushing plane. Larger and larger it loomed as it slanted downward toward the racing target. There was a tense hush throughout the ship. Then, a short distance off the starboard bow came a splash and a brief spout of bubbling water as the bomb fell harmlessly into the sea where the pilot expected to find his target, but didn't.

When the program of naval expansion was first under discussion by the company and the Navy back in 1939, it was proposed to produce the new turbine-propulsion equipment at Schenectady where similar turbines had already been built. Later, as the shipbuilding program continued to expand, it was decided to transfer the manufacture of the destroyer equipment to the Erie Works. A building there, formerly used for transformer manufacture but then being utilized only for storage of refrigerator cabinets, was equipped for making destroyer turbines. An additional building was later built and equipped for the same purpose.

Each destroyer required two 30,000-horsepower turbine drives. The first order given to the Erie Works covered equipment for 6 ships. Within a short time this was increased to 47 ships. Then it was jumped to 175. By the end of the war the program amounted to a total of 200 ships.

Veteran of more than a dozen battles, with a mileage of 158,911 to her credit during her first two years at sea, the U.S.S. *Jenkins* was typical of the many G-E equipped destroyers. Despite a minimum of upkeep during this period, the condition of her turbines and generators was "almost as good as new" according to Rear Admiral E. L. Cochrane, Chief of the Bureau of Ships.

The initial turbine program for heavy cruisers called for equipment for eight ships. Here again it was first planned that this equipment should be built at Schenectady. Because the equipment for the cruisers was much the same as that for destroyers, the principal difference being in the number of units per ship, the cruiser program was superimposed on the Erie destroyer program. Eventually this involved a total of 22 cruisers. Similar equipment was also produced at Erie for 2 carriers converted from cruisers. Schenectady built all the turbines for 6 battleships, 10 aircraft carriers, 15 cruisers, and 8 destroyers.

By the end of the war, General Electric had built 27-million horsepower of turbine-propulsion equipment for the new Navy. This was the equivalent of all the turbine equipment shipped from Schenectady during the entire history of the turbine business from its beginnings at the turn of the century. In other words the company produced more for the Navy in World War II than it had done for the power industry in 40 years.

A RACE AGAINST TIME

In the latter part of 1941, attacks by German submarines were causing such tremendous shipping losses in the North Atlantic that the whole scheme of Allied strategy was threatened with disaster. The rate of sinkings of merchant ships was more than twice as high as the combined capacity of British and American shipyards to replace them. The convoy system, which had been expected to provide an answer to the submarine menace, was rapidly breaking down because there were not enough escort vessels to protect the convoys adequately, and the U-boat skippers knew it.

The Allies could not go out and hunt the submarines. All they could do was to stay on the defensive, waiting until the subs chose the moment to strike. On more than one occasion a pack of U-boats is reported to have stood off out of range of a convoy and openly taunted the ships by radio, promising, as soon as night fell, to come in for a killing.

The Navy decided that the solution of the problem lay in the creation of a large fleet of ships of an entirely new type called the "destroyer escort." This new vessel somewhat resembled the British "corvette." It was to be a little smaller than the latest type of destroyer, though larger than those of World War I, with a steel hull having a length of approximately 300 feet and a beam of 35 feet. It was to be fast, seaworthy, and fitted with the deadliest armament ever mounted on a ship of that size.

This armament included guns heavy enough to enable the destroyer escort to shoot it out with a submarine on the surface, antiaircraft guns of various calibers, depth charges, and torpedo tubes. These ships were designed strictly for attack. At the first hint of danger to the cargo vessels they were protecting, they were to dash into battle with the lurking U-boats.

The propulsion machinery had to be such as to enable the DE to maneuver more readily than most other ocean-going craft, and to excel the submarine's best speed. Equally important, the ship had to be so designed that it could be built rapidly by mass-production methods and so that this could be done in shipyards that were not equipped to construct larger warships.

DESTROYER ESCORT PROGRAM

In designing the destroyer escort, the naval architects originally planned for geared-turbine propulsion. But it was found that the gear-making capacity of the country was already overloaded with prior Navy contracts. To avoid the gear-making bottleneck, General Electric suggested that the DE's be provided with turbine-electric drive. At a conference of Navy officials and representatives of the company in Schenectady on Jan. 13, 1942, this idea was approved and the company was given the job of producing the equipment. At the same time orders were given to other manufacturers to build diesel-driven destroyer escorts.

General Electric's assignment called for equipping a total of 305 ships, 50 to be completed in 1943, 150 in 1944, and 105 in 1945. The company was to provide two 4,600-kilowatt turbine-generator units per ship together with propulsion motors and control, auxiliary power sets, cable, voltage regulators, amplidyne-excitation system, switchgear, motors and control for auxiliary drives, and ship fittings, such as fuse boxes, relays, and circuit breakers.

This was an unprecedented undertaking. And it came at the time when the company was already engaged in a tremendous program of turbine building for battleships, cruisers, carriers, and destroyers. Plans were immediately drawn up for a new $16,000,000 plant at Syracuse having more than 15 acres of floor space. It was built, equipped with machine tools, manned with 3,000 new employees, and was turning out equipment of a brand new design in the unbelievably short period of 9 months. Appropriately enough, the first DE turbine-generator set was delivered to the Navy from Syracuse on Dec. 7, 1942, the first anniversary of Pearl Harbor.

Meanwhile, production of these units was under way at Erie, too. And propulsion motors were being made at Pittsfield. Equipment for four ships was delivered in 1942. The next year the program really hit its stride. A telegram had been received from Rear Admiral E. L. Cochrane, calling upon the company's workers to speed up production.

The telegram said:

No graver problem faces our forces than the submarine menace. To meet this crisis, to curtail the loss of crews, the destruction of ships, and the waste of cargos, we must sink the enemy's subs faster than they can be built. The escort vessels are part of the Navy's answer to the submarine. We need these ships now. It is not enough to build and launch the hulls. They must be fitted out and put into service with the utmost speed. The component parts which you are making play a vital role in fitting these ships for sea duty. Can you increase your output? Your future production records will be your answer!

Efforts were intensified. Production was already ahead of schedule, but it was speeded up still more. For the year 1943, instead of providing the equipment for 50 ships as promised, the company did so for 162 ships, this work being divided about equally between Syracuse and Erie.

In December of that year, the destroyer escort *Reynolds*, built at Hingham, Mass., was delivered to the Navy just 25 days after keel laying. This was about half the time required to build the destroyer *Reid*, a smaller vessel, which held the production speed record for World War I.

At sea the destroyer escorts soon made their presence felt. One of the early DE's, the U.S.S. *Buckley*, took part in a particularly thrilling battle in the North Atlantic. One moonlight night when the ship was engaged in convoy work a Navy flier sighted a submarine on the surface a few miles away from the convoy and radioed the news to the escort vessel. Instantly the *Buckley* left its place with the convoy and headed for the spot where the U-boat had been seen. In a matter of minutes she drew within range and delivered a salvo from her deck guns. One shot scored a direct hit on

These 16-inch guns of one of the largest U.S. battleships in action against the Japs were aimed at an unseen target by radar, which knows no night.

*Electric motors opened the bow doors and lowered the ramp for
this tank to rumble ashore on a Normandy beach.*

Flying Fortresses raid Europe in broad daylight, escorted by long-range, high-altitude, turbosupercharged Lightnings.

Enormous but precise—gears for ship propulsion as large as 200-inch diameter had to be cut to .003-inch tolerances.

Armatures for marine motors—seven units which will furnish 54,000 horsepower to drive fast new tankers.

Power for the Navy's speedy new ships—turbine rotors on the assembly floor at the Erie Works.

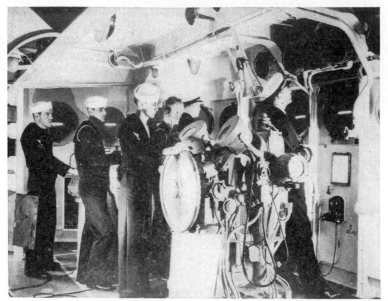

Electric instruments and equipment on navigating bridge of U.S.S. North Carolina reflect extent to which ships depend upon electricity.

Navy switchgear on assembly floor. G.E.'s Philadelphia Works produced 33,814 switchgear units for some 4000 ships.

G-E fire control equipment on this type of ship included the gun director mounted forward of the mast and hydraulic control for 5-inch guns.

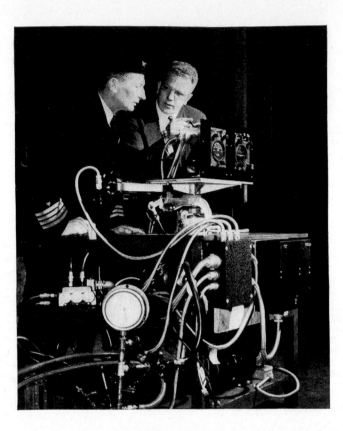

Automatic pilot to keep a plane continuously on a predetermined course, being inspected by Capt. J. S. Evans, Inspector of Naval Material.

Turbosuperchargers ready for shipment. Additional power which G-E turbosuperchargers gave planes aggregated more than 160,-000,000 horsepower.

the forecastle of the German craft. The sub tried to run, twisting and turning to evade the moon track on the water. The U-boat's torpedoes and deck and machine guns were fired at the *Buckley*, but their aim was inaccurate and little damage was done.

The captain of the *Buckley* was determined to ram the sub and he drove his ship forward regardless of the German firing. In a minute he had caught her and the *Buckley*'s prow plunged into the forecastle of the U-boat. Fighting Germans swarmed aboard the escort, but they were quickly subdued by the American sailors.

To avoid more boarders the *Buckley* backed off, and again the U-boat tried to flee. But she could not get away from the fast American ship. The *Buckley* hung close to her, firing again and again at almost point-blank range. After three direct hits by the DE's 3-inch deck guns, the sub, spouting flames, plowed under the surface. A couple of minutes later a heavy underwater explosion churned the sea over a wide area.

Even before the year 1943 ended the tide was turning against the submarine and the need for additional DE's began to taper off. By the middle of May, 1944, the Navy felt able to cancel orders for 61 ships, reducing the total from 305 to 244. Erie produced no destroyer-escort equipment that year but Syracuse continued production until August, turning out equipment for the last 78 ships.

TRAINING THE PERSONNEL

It was early realized that these new convoy guardians would be of little use without properly trained crews. As the Navy had few men acquainted with electric ship propulsion, the General Electric Company agreed to establish a school for training the nucleus of engine-room crews for these destroyer escorts.

The first class of 28 Navy men reported at the Schenectady

Works in December, 1942, for a 4 weeks' training course, but the school was soon moved to the Syracuse Works where better facilities were available.

There classrooms had been constructed and furnished with charts, photographs, mechanical models of equipment, and other visual training aids. On the factory floor outside the classroom was a duplicate of the complete engine room of a destroyer escort. The equipment included the 6,000-horsepower turbine-generator set, condenser, main propulsion motor, ship-service turbine-generator set, main control board, and all the necessary auxiliaries. Steam power and shore power were furnished to the simulated engine room from the general factory supply. The course of instruction was divided into lecture periods, inspection of manufacturing processes, and actual operation of the engine room.

This "school ship" was named the U.S.S. *Knox* in honor of Frank Knox, then Secretary of the Navy. Between the date of its christening in the spring of 1943 and the graduation of its final class in the fall of 1944, it provided training for 2,523 officers and men of the Navy. Four weeks of training in this school gave the men a better understanding of the turbine-electric equipment and its operation than could have been attained in a year of ordinary operation on shipboard. This understanding later paid big dividends in the splendid performance records of the ships as they guarded the vital supply lines that practically circled the globe—across the North Atlantic, through the Arctic Ocean to Murmansk, to the Mediterranean, to the Middle East around the Cape of Good Hope, and across the broad Pacific.

TRIBUTE FROM SECRETARY FORRESTAL

Commenting on the company's work for the Navy, Secretary James Forrestal, who succeeded Knox, wrote to General Electric's President, Charles E. Wilson, at the end of the war saying:

Our strategy of attack, with all the risks it implied, was made possible by our ability to build—or, if necessary to rebuild—a vast fleet ranging from aircraft carriers and battleships to small boats.

Among the companies which gave our fleet the power to attack, yours has been preeminent. You and all the men and women who have worked with you deserve, therefore, to carry into peace a special pride in a great national achievement.

3

Ships Behind the Headlines

AMONG THE MANY UNPLEASANT SURPRISES which came to the Japanese as the war progressed, none did more to upset their plans than the U.S. Navy's Task Force 58. This was by far the most powerful and destructive unit in the whole history of naval warfare. Its activities included the sinking of some 30 Japanese ships and the destruction of 757 Jap planes.

When Task Force 58 was at sea, the whole ocean from horizon to horizon, appeared to be covered with ships—carriers, battleships, cruisers, destroyers, and their auxiliaries. A single look at this huge armada, and anyone could tell who was going to win the war. But the secret of success was not the array of combat ships alone. It was the highly organized system of fleet auxiliaries that enabled Task Force 58 to operate successfully so many thousands of miles from its home base.

FUEL FOR TASK FORCE 58

Task Force 58 carried its fuel, food, and replacement aircraft and pilots wherever it went. Operating as a tail-end group in the force was the "fleet train" with the necessary supplies for the combat ships. It had its own carrier protection, its own cruisers, and its own destroyers.

Behind all this lay the vital problem of fuel—fuel for the ships and fuel for the planes. Without an adequate supply of fuel, Task Force 58 would never have been able to steam thousands of miles and do battle with the Japs in their home waters. And it had the fuel it needed because it had a fleet of fast tankers that could keep up with the swift warships and refuel them whenever necessary. The development of these fast tankers is a story of the combined efforts of the Navy, the Maritime Commission, the shipbuilders, the oil companies, the General Electric Company, and other manufacturers.

Back in the 1930's, opinion was divided on the question whether a fast tanker or a slow tanker was more economical to operate. Practically all the 300 U.S. tankers then in existence were old and slow. But some oil men believed that fast tankers, though more expensive to build, would be a sound investment. In 1936, General Electric was asked to design and build a turbine-electric drive for a fast new tanker, the *J. W. Van Dyke*. This proved so satisfactory that during the next five years, eight similar tankers were built and equipped with turbine-electric drive.

ACCELERATED TANKER PROGRAM

Then came the war. German submarines began to take a heavy toll of tankers in the Atlantic. That the United States would ultimately become an active participant in the war appeared extremely likely. The Maritime Commission, acting in concert with the armed forces, decided to build up the American Merchant Marine and placed an order for fifty new high-speed tankers.

This was an ambitious project, bristling with difficulties. One of the biggest was the procurement of the necessary propulsion equipment. Turbine-gear drive was generally regarded as the most suitable type of propulsion for tankers, but turbine gears were urgently needed for the Navy and for the cargo ships of the Maritime Commission's great expansion program. There simply were not enough gear-making facilities in the country to build gears for all the needed ships.

Some other solution of the problem had to be found. So the head of the shipbuilding company responsible for building the tankers called General Electric's J. W. Belanger, manager of the Federal and Marine Division, and outlined the Maritime Commission's new program.

"Can you build the turbine-electric drive for these ships?" Belanger was asked.

"Yes, we can," he replied promptly.

At Schenectady and Lynn and Pittsfield and Philadelphia and Erie, machines that had been making apparatus for peacetime use were turned rapidly to the production of turbine-electric propulsion equipment for the ships of the new American tanker fleet.

The decision of the Maritime Commission was made none too soon. Japan's attack on Pearl Harbor came before the year was up. American tankers immediately became the prey of German submarines. Day after day ships steaming up the Atlantic Coast from the Gulf of Mexico were attacked and set on fire. Ships crossing the North Atlantic were torpedoed and sunk in increasing numbers. The country's fleet of tankers was steadily reduced.

The fifty new tankers then building were not enough. The Maritime Commission called on the shipbuilders for more and more hulls, and on General Electric for more and more turbine-electric propulsion equipment—the equipment that would drive tankers at such speed that they could avoid the deadly submarines.

Manufacturing tempo increased. In ever greater quantity the vital propulsion machinery rolled off the production lines. Before the war was ended the company had supplied turbine-electric drive for 378 tankers. Appropriately enough, the 100th tanker launched at Swan Island on the Pacific Coast was christened the *W. L. R. Emmet,* in honor of the farsighted G-E engineer who pioneered the turbine-electric drive for ships.

SAFE TO TRAVEL ALONE

Wartime tankers were ships of 16,000 dead-weight tons, designed to carry 135,000 barrels of oil. For most of them the driving mechanism comprised a turbine-generator set and a 6,000-horsepower synchronous propulsion motor. One lot of 44, however, had 10,000-horsepower motors. The official— but not the top—speed of the 6,000-horsepower ships was 15½ knots. The ships with larger motors had an official speed of 17¼ knots, though they, too, could travel faster if necessary.

Speed served them well. The prewar tankers, running at about 10 knots, were easy prey for enemy submarines that could do 10 knots submerged and twice that speed on the surface. Their only hope of safety was in traveling in convoys. The new tankers, on the other hand, were equipped with antiaircraft and deck guns fore and aft, and, with their higher speed, could take care of themselves.

"I've seen tankers torpedoed on each side of me," said one of the veteran sailors of this service. "I've seen sailors burned to death by flaming oil. I might have had the same fate if our tanker hadn't been fast enough to outrun a sub.

"We spotted this sub in a beam of moonlight off our starboard bow. He was on the surface charging his batteries. We immediately changed our course and he started to chase us. We were lucky to have a new tanker with a top speed of 21 knots, and we were too fast for him. Evidently he heard us radio for destroyer help, because pretty soon he gave up the chase and submerged."

Some of the new tankers were turned over to the Navy to serve the fleet. Some were sold to oil and tanker companies.

Most of them, however, were operated by private companies under charter from the War Shipping Administration. When carrying fuel across the Pacific to advance Army and Navy bases, or when operating between the Gulf of Mexico and Atlantic Coast ports, they ran free. Only when used in trans-Atlantic service were they convoyed—often in special fast convoys—for there they were up against a greater concentration of enemy submarines, and also of enemy planes.

In addition to the service they rendered in the transportation of fuel, the tankers did extra duty as freighters. They were provided with special, latticelike "Meccano" decks on a level with the catwalks, on which great numbers of planes, trucks, PT boats, etc., were piled. Without this arrangement the Army Air Forces would have had hard work to handle their overseas shipments of airplanes. And with it all the turbine-electric tankers proved more economical to operate than the old tankers because they were faster and more efficient.

TURBINES FOR THE MERCHANT MARINE

Along with tankers, the nation needed cargo ships. After having been one of the world's leading maritime nations in the early part of the nineteenth century, the United States gradually lost interest in seafaring activities and centered its attention on industrial developments within its own borders. So, by the early part of the twentieth century its fleet of ocean-going merchant ships had dwindled to almost nothing. A frenzied, but on the whole successful effort was made to correct this situation during World War I. A fleet of new ships was built—of steel, of wood, and even of concrete. Those of wood and of concrete never amounted to much, but the end of that war left the country with a sizable fleet of ocean-going steel ships.

Once more the country lost interest in maritime activities. Its war-built ships were put in storage in little-used rivers and harbors where they were allowed to rust and decay while the ships of other nations carried America's overseas freight. Many farseeing people deplored this failure to utilize the wartime cargo fleet, but shipping interests generally contended that the American vessels were too slow for profitable operation.

A serious attempt to rebuild the country's Merchant Marine was started in 1936. Under the sponsorship of the newly created United States Maritime Commission a sprinkling of new ships was constructed and put in operation. This undertaking was just commencing to show results when World War II began in Europe. It quickly became evident that the country was going to need a great many more ships than it then had. Thereupon the Maritime Commission embarked on a vast program of expansion for the Merchant Marine.

Reading from experience, the commission decided that the new ships should be big enough and fast enough for profitable operation in peacetime as well as in wartime. To ensure this the ships were to be equipped with the most modern turbine-gear drive. In midsummer of 1941, Admiral Emory Land, chairman of the commission, notified G.E. that:

The General Electric Company has been selected to build a plant suitable for the manufacture of merchant marine propelling equipment at the rate of 100 turbines and 50 gears per year, delivery to commence as soon as possible, but not later than the first of August, 1942. This plant is to cost approximately $22,000,-000.

Instructions further directed that work be started immediately pending the settlement of final details.

Design work was started on a new building at Erie to supplement facilities at Lynn already operating to capacity. Ground was broken at once. Delay was encountered in securing the necessary steel, which was not delivered until November. Erection was started immediately and was completed within a month. Meanwhile orders had been received for 100 turbines for cargo vessels of the types known as "C-2" and "C-3." Preliminary work on these turbines was started in other buildings. The new building was completed and formally occupied in February, 1942. The first C-3 turbine went to test on April 23 and was shipped in May, more than 2 months ahead of the deadline set by the Maritime Commission.

During the remainder of the year 1942, twenty-four more C-3 units were turned out. The next year the production was 112, equally divided between C-2's and C-3's. Then another type was added, the Victory AP-2. Altogether, 183 units were produced in 1944 and 95 in 1945 up to the time when the progress of the war permitted relaxation of the program. In all, the Erie Works turned out a total of 415 sets of propulsion turbines for the new cargo fleet in addition to the large number made at Lynn.

These fast cargo vessels were among the more than 1,000 ships in the armada for the North African landing, first decisive step toward victory in Europe. They were present for the landings in Sicily and on the Normandy beaches. In the Pacific they participated in every major campaign. Without them the United States' 4 million men could never have been transported and maintained overseas as the greatest water-borne invading force in the history of the world.

DIESEL-ELECTRIC DRIVE FOR SHIPS

An outstanding development of the war was the great increase in the use of diesel-electric propulsion equipment for auxiliary ships. The first installation of this kind had been made in 1920. During the next 20 years General Electric furnished approximately a hundred equipments with a combined total of 180,000 horsepower. Then the rush began. The equipment supplied in 1941 and 1942 had greater aggregate horsepower than all that had been installed previously. The next 2 years were even busier. For the 5 war years the total was well over 1,500,000 horsepower.

This diesel-electric propulsion equipment was used on a wide variety of vessels. Among them were 30 powerful fleet tugs of the U.S. Navy, equipped with 3,000-horsepower engines, and 77 harbor tugs of somewhat smaller size. Approximately 40 salvage vessels equipped for the Navy had twin-screw propulsion and four generators per ship to provide ample power when called upon to stand by a vessel in distress or to operate in a heavy sea. There were also 44 net tenders for the arduous work of raising and lowering the heavy submarine nets that guarded the entrances to important harbors. A total of 85 mine sweepers were equipped to aid in keeping channels safe and clear for the steady stream of vessels entering and leaving busy ports.

SUBMARINES ON THE SEVEN SEAS

Diesel-electric propulsion equipment was used on submarines too. Exploits of the German U-boats focused a great deal of attention on that nation's progress in undersea warfare, but in actual performance the submarines of the United States Navy were second to none. They sailed the seven seas and even made forays into some of the rivers and harbors of the Japanese home islands. They sank a tremendous tonnage of enemy vessels, both warships and merchant ships. More than any other type of vessel, they penetrated into the enemy's back yard. Many of the names of these submarines are listed forever on the honor roll of the United States Navy.

At the close of World War I, the United States had a sizable fleet of submarines equipped with a so-called "mechanical drive." This was an arrangement whereby the propeller shaft was mechanically connected to a diesel engine for surface operation or turned, when under water, by an electric motor actuated by storage batteries. When the submarine was at a standstill, the diesel engine could be used to drive the motor as a dynamo for charging the batteries.

While this was a satisfactory arrangement in many respects, the power possible per hull was limited because the direct-connected diesel engines had to operate at relatively slow speeds to match the permissible propeller speeds. This drawback led the Navy in 1931 to study the possibilities of a high-speed diesel connected to an electric generator that would supply power to a motor on the propeller shaft.

The submarine S-20, a ship built some years earlier, was selected for experiment. Originally this ship had two screws, each with the so-called "mechanical drive." It was decided to rebuild one of these screws for "electric drive."

At this point, the General Electric Company, which had participated in previous submarine building for the Navy, made the suggestion that best results in the S-20 experiment could be obtained by using a small, high-speed electric motor connected to the propeller shaft through reduction gears. Such an arrangement, it was thought, would be most effective as a means of conserving both weight and space.

Representatives of the Navy visited Schenectady to discuss the proposal in detail with the company's engineers. Convinced that the idea was worth trying, the Navy proceeded to write specifications and invite bids. Three other companies submitted bids in response to the invitation, and the contract was awarded to General Electric. Construction of the motors was commenced immediately at Schenectady, while the reduction gears were started at the River Works, Lynn.

ADOPTION OF ELECTRIC DRIVE

Operation of the electrically driven propeller on the S-20 proved so satisfactory that, in 1933, the Navy asked for bids on four new vessels to be equipped in the same way. General Electric did not build the propulsion equipment for any of these ships, but the next year was awarded the contracts on three of the six submarines laid down by the Navy. These were the SS-176, 177, and 178.

The experience gained in building this equipment was of great help to the company. Space limitations imposed extremely difficult design requirements. Problems arose in connection with both mechanical and electrical operation. All the difficulties were overcome, however, and these machines set the style for many that followed. From 1935 until the end of the war General Electric participated in the building of every lot of new submarines ordered by the Navy. By the end of the war the company had built propulsion equipment for 174 submarines, or two-thirds of the entire number constructed since 1933.

The Navy accorded high praise to the performance of this propulsion equipment. The U.S.S. *Guitarro*, S-363, for example, in 10 months of action sank two Japanese cruisers, three destroyers, eight transports and cargo ships, and two tankers. During this long period of strenuous combat service, with the *Guitarro* frequently pursuing enemy targets and evading hostile attack, the main motors, in the Navy's own words, "proved 100 per cent efficient."

EPIC OF THE *SQUALUS*

Among the submarines built during the Navy's prewar expansion program was the U.S.S. *Squalus*. In the early summer of 1939 she was considered the latest word in underseas craft. One day during diving practice off Portsmouth, N.H., she suddenly and inexplicably sank in 240 feet of water. The Navy rushed its special underwater rescue chamber to the scene. Despite the great depth of water the rescuers succeeded in saving the lives of 33 of her crew of 59 in the first operation of its kind in history.

Then began the long, tedious job of salvaging the ship, herself. In this, too, the depth of water was a serious problem. After repeated efforts, however, the submarine was finally brought to the surface on September 13, sixteen weeks after sinking. She was put in dry dock, and her reconditioning commenced.

The electric propulsion equipment was sent back to Schenectady for overhaul. In spite of its having been under water for nearly 4 months it was found to be in relatively good condition. After drying out, the motors ran satisfactorily, but for additional safety each unit was taken apart, thoroughly cleaned, reinsulated, and reassembled. The overhauled equipment was then returned to the Navy Yard at Portsmouth and installed in the reconditioned hull. A few months later the old *Squalus* was put back in commission as the *Sailfish*.

Under her new name she joined the Pacific Fleet and played an effective part in the grim battle against the Japanese. In that struggle fate gave her a rare opportunity to erase the memory of her early, disastrous sinking.

In the midst of a typhoon, tremendous seas, and a driving rain she encountered a fleet of Jap ships. The commander on the bridge could see nothing but blackness and water everywhere, but radar told him of the presence of the enemy vessels. Waiting patiently to attack the largest target shown on the radar screen, the submarine dodged and submerged as the smaller ships passed by. Finally the big target came within range. It was a 22,500-ton aircraft carrier of the *Kasuga* class. The sub fired her torpedoes and heard the impact of two hits. Within seconds she was being attacked with depth charges, but none did any damage.

After about half an hour the *Sailfish* surfaced again to look for the crippled carrier. She found her circling slowly. As the visibility improved somewhat, the *Sailfish* fired two more torpedoes. The carrier replied with a rain of shellfire, but apparently did not know the whereabouts of the *Sailfish* as the shooting was aimed in all directions.

The visibility continued to improve. The Japs located the

Sailfish and the random firing was replaced by accurate aiming. But the submarine could really see her quarry now. Moving cautiously but steadily she crept to within less than a mile of the wounded carrier. Then, taking careful aim, she released all her torpedoes. Hits were heard, followed by exceptionally loud explosions aboard the big ship. The carrier began to break up and 9 minutes later disappeared beneath the waves. For this exploit the *Sailfish* received the Presidential Unit Citation.

Quietly and without publicity the Navy's submarines and the auxiliary and cargo ships did a magnificent job. Few of these ships ever figured in newspaper headlines, but their work was vital to the successful operation of the Navy.

4

Equipment for Ships of War

LESS DRAMATIC than the part played by ship-propulsion equipment, but equally important, was that played by other shipboard electric apparatus. Applications of electricity included radio and radar, lighting, ammunition hoists, fire control, searchlights, steering gear, X ray, ventilating fans, welding sets, cooking ranges, refrigerators, laundry machinery, and an endless variety of cranes, winches, and windlasses. The quantities of this equipment that General Electric was called upon to produce were enormous. More than 23,000 motors, ranging from one-half to 250 horsepower, were supplied to drive the fans for shipboard ventilating systems. Remote control was built for the steering mechanisms on over a thousand ships of the Navy. Erie Works turned out some 20,000 motors for the Maritime Commission's cargo vessels. Philadelphia Works turned out 33,814 switchgear units for some 4,000 ships.

PANEL BOARDS FOR THE NAVY

Unusual requirements had to be met in the design of power- and light-control panel boards for the Navy. The burning of the giant steamship *Normandie* in the early part of 1942 had focused attention sharply on dangers accom-

Mighty ships of the world's most powerful Navy heading for battle stations in the campaign to recapture the Philippines.

End of a Nazi raider—planes from an escort carrier circle over spot where U-boat sank.

Carrying the attack against the enemy. Ships of the U.S. Third Fleet support a landing on a Jap-held island.

Launching on June 7, 1941, of the G-E equipped U.S.S. South Dakota, which later became widely known as the mysterious "Battleship X."

OFFICIAL U.S. NAVY PHOTO

*Six months ahead of schedule—the 35,000-ton
U.S.S. Washington equipped with G-E turbine-
gear drive, switchgear and auxiliary apparatus
being commissioned May 15, 1941.*

*First of an entirely new class of large cruiser, the U.S.S. Alaska was
bigger and more powerful than any previous type of U.S. cruiser.*

Beauty in metal—expert workmanship was required to produce this turbine rotor for one of the heavy cruisers.

Cutting ship propulsion gears at Lynn. Atmospheric conditions must be controlled within narrow limits to assure watchmakers' precision in tooth spacing.

*With three of its four turbines crippled in battle,
the U.S.S. Independence limped home at 17 knots
on its one remaining unit.*

*DD-435, U.S.S. Grayson, one of 200 fast destroyers
equipped with G-E turbine-gear drive.*

*Fast, seaworthy and fitted with the deadliest arm-
ament ever mounted on a ship of that size, the
destroyer escort was a highly effective weapon
against submarines.*

*Launching of the U.S.S. John D. Buckley, one of
the first of the great new fleet of destroyer escorts.*

Built by mass production methods in shipyards not equipped to construct larger warships, destroyer escorts were delivered in record time.

This completely equipped destroyer escort engine room at G.E.'s Syracuse Plant served as training school for 2523 officers and men of the Navy.

panying the use of inflammable materials in ship construction. On that occasion many fire fighters were overcome by the noxious fumes of burning panel boards made of phenolic materials which gave off carbon monoxide and other poisonous gases.

Recognizing the hazard involved in the use of such materials on warships where fires often occur during battle, the Navy asked the plastics industry to study the problem of developing plastics materials that would eliminate the danger. The material sought had to be fire resistant and nontoxic, have good insulation properties, high impact strength, and be easily moldable.

Experiments by General Electric indicated that it would be impossible to use any appreciable amount of organic filler in either a laminated plastic or a molding compound without producing a material that would give off toxic gases if it caught fire. The chemists then turned to the use of inorganic filler materials such as asbestos and glass. After a period of research they selected asbestos as the filler they wanted because it embodied all the specifications—relatively high flame resistance, low toxicity, easy moldability, and good shock resistance. The asbestos fibres were bound together with phenolic resins to make a series of plastics with various shock resistances.

In the course of the investigations a peculiar fact was discovered. Experiments showed that the asbestos had to be woven into fabric first and then chopped to give the requisite mechanical strength. Unwoven asbestos, for some reason, did not have the necessary strength. At first the asbestos producers refused to believe that their material had to be woven to definite specifications, only to be chopped up for plastic filler later. In the end, however, they were convinced that this was the only way to get the desired result.

Panel boards of the new plastics were turned out in tremendous numbers by the company for the Navy. Actual battle service proved their worth, particularly on aircraft carriers which suffered serious fires as a result of bombing attacks. In fact the miraculous return of carriers such as the U.S.S. *Franklin* and *Bunker Hill,* which were the targets of devastating attacks by Japanese suicide planes, would probably not have been possible if their electrical panel boards had not been made of such fire-resistant material.

SHOCKPROOFING SHIPBOARD LAMPS

Shipboard lighting was one of the most important uses of electricity. A battleship might require as many as 20,000 lamp bulbs. Usually a big ship carried two to three times that number in order to have plenty of replacements. Smaller ships required fewer lamps, but even the smallest required a great many for ordinary lighting and for signal lights, warning lights, marker lights, searchlights, and other purposes.

Prior to World War II, the standard rough-service electric lamp satisfactorily withstood the normal shocks and vibrations of a warship. It even proved fairly reliable under the shock of the occasional firing of the ship's guns. But the war brought shocks of greater magnitude and frequency than had ever been encountered before. Firing of broadsides for hours at a stretch became commonplace. Worse yet, innumerable direct hits were registered on ships by gunfire, torpedoes, and bombs from airplanes. Near misses often shook a warship as violently as a direct hit. Lamps had to be built capable of withstanding these shocks.

To meet this grave need, engineers of the General Electric Lamp Department developed a high-impact filament lamp with a rubber-cushioned base. In appearance the new lamp closely resembled the ordinary household electric lamp except for having a thick band of rubber surrounding the neck between the metal base and the glass bulb. This rubber skirt proved to be sufficiently elastic to absorb violent shocks and yet was sufficiently rigid to prevent the bulb from whipping back and forth and setting up harmonic vibrations that would quickly have destroyed the filament.

These sturdy 50-watt lamps rendered dependable service on ships of the United States Navy in virtually every corner of the world. They kept right on burning brightly despite exploding depth charges, bombings, shellings, and collisions. Time and time again they saved an engine room or battle station from going dark at a critical moment when light was vitally needed. "The performance of the Lamp Department in developing these highly specialized items," said the Bureau of Ships, "placing them in production, and delivering them on schedule merits particular commendation."

Electric running lights were especially important to prevent collisions of ships traveling in groups. For that reason special two-filament lamps were used for these lights. When one filament burned out, an auxiliary filament automatically came into service. Seldom, if ever, did both filaments burn out during the same 24 hours. Thus a daily inspection almost certainly assured that the running lights were in working order.

REFRIGERATION AT SEA

On shipboard, electric refrigeration established new dietary and health standards. Sailors on the larger vessels of the United States Navy had for years before the war been able to enjoy a "frosted chocolate" or a dish of ice cream wherever the ship might happen to be. This "home-town drugstore" touch in fighting ships proved so popular that the Navy undertook to provide ice cream making equipment for practically all its combat vessels.

A special type of equipment included a 2½-gallon batch freezer, a 30-gallon hardening section, and a 20-gallon dispensing section. In the hardening section the temperature was maintained at 15 degrees below zero, while in the dispensing section it was 5 degrees above zero. Refrigeration was provided by a 2-horsepower G-E air-cooled marine condensing unit. This had a two-speed motor that permitted operation of the unit at half speed when the freezer was not in use.

Ice cream making was only one of many applications of air-conditioning and refrigeration equipment on vessels of the Navy and Merchant Marine. Artificial cold was required to preserve blood plasma and other medical supplies, maintain proper atmosphere conditions in ammunition storage spaces, sick bays, food-storage compartments, radar rooms, control rooms, and areas which might be completely closed off during combat.

Failure of a ship's refrigeration system meant rapid spoilage of the vessel's food supply and of other perishable materials, particularly if the ship was in tropical waters. Great care was therefore taken to ensure adequate provision against breakdown. Usually the refrigeration system was designed to include duplicate, oversized compressors and condensers so arranged that either set could be used in emergencies at full capacity, or both sets could be used at reduced capacity for normal conditions. Extremely rigid specifications controlled the manufacture throughout.

Two new types of ships proved to be vital to success in the Pacific, the "attack troop transport" and the "attack cargo ship." These two types operated together as part of a task force. The attack transport carried what was known as a combat team—a complete unit of Marines or other troops equipped for battle. It was designed to provide living accommodations for the troops, and at the same time was equipped with landing craft and tank lighters to carry the troops and tanks to the beachhead. The attack cargo ship carried the ammunition, vehicles, food, and medical supplies—in other words, all the equipment and material necessary to keep the combat units going until they gained a toe hold on enemy territory. These ships were "combat loaded" so that the equipment needed first could be unloaded first.

For an amphibious operation the task force was made up of battleships, aircraft carriers, cruisers, and destroyers along with the transports and cargo ships. The warships stood off-shore and softened up the enemy by a heavy bombardment with their big guns. Then the attacking force landed from small craft. Finally, the transports and cargo ships moved close in toward the beach to disembark more men, supplies, and equipment.

On each of these transports and cargo ships were five large refrigerated spaces—dairy room, vegetable room, fruit room, meat room, and an ice maker capable of turning out 250 pounds of ice every 3 hours. Two compressor units were used on each ship. These were built at the Winter Street Plant in Fort Wayne, control apparatus being furnished by the Bloomfield Works. This equipment permitted the men of the task forces to have fresh food however far away they might be from a home base.

Refrigeration also went to sea in "Victory" ships. When the U.S. Maritime Commission undertook to build its big fleet, speed was of first importance, so G-E engineers collaborated in the design of prefabricated unit refrigeration equipment. Each ship had two low-temperature rooms cooled by pipe coils, three moderate-temperature rooms kept at about 40 degrees by unit coolers, and an ice freezer.

Installation was normally a time-consuming job. However, by prefabricating all the elements of the system, such as the duplex condensing units, pipe coils, and control cabinets, installation could be made in the vessel in a fraction of the time required to install the usual ship refrigeration system.

ELECTRIC SHIP FITTINGS

Part of the seagoing electric equipment produced by the company during the war was similar to equipment that had been built in prewar days. The rest of it was radically new and different. When Pearl Harbor necessitated a gigantic expansion of both fighting and merchant fleets, the success of the program was endangered by a critical shortage of ship fittings, assemblages of switches, fuses, circuit breakers, relays, and other items in watertight boxes. Existing manufacturers did not have the capacity to meet the shipyards' skyrocketing demands. Not the least of the problems resulted from a sudden decision by the Bureau of Ships that most of the electrical ship fittings, which had previously been made of cast aluminum and brass, should be redesigned so that they could be made of shockproof sheet steel. So the Navy went to General Electric with the problem.

"Your Appliance and Merchandise Department," they said, "is an old hand at making wiring devices and other electrical products. Would you consider redesigning and producing electrical ship fittings for this program?"

Although an affirmative answer meant that the company would enter a field requiring new machinery and tools, additional draftsmen, and special training of supervisory and factory personnel, the company said, "Yes."

At Bridgeport the engineering organization went to work on the new designs and the manufacturing organization began to acquire machines and tools for the production job. One of the appliance warehouses was emptied and converted into a working area. Men and women were trained for their new jobs.

The original order covered 176 different kinds of fittings to be used on the new destroyer escorts. First deliveries were scheduled for August, but early in May a representative of one of the shipyards rushed to the Bridgeport Works with a plea for enough fittings to complete immediately the ships which his yard was building. Despite the fact that the Ship Fittings Division had no finished tools, few machines, and only a handful of skilled workers, the shipbuilder's representative left with the assurance that his order would be filled. And it was—by hand.

Two months later, production of the entire line of ship fittings was well under way. Before the end of 1942, production had climbed as high as 40,000 finished items per week. The next year it hit 50,000 a week.

During the last 3 years of the war General Electric supplied more electrical ship fittings than any other manufacturer in the country. Altogether the company made over five hundred different kinds of fittings, ranging from push buttons to signal lights. Its wiring and lighting devices were serving on LCI's (landing craft, infantry), LCV's (landing craft, vehicle), DE's, submarines, destroyers, cruisers, and aircraft carriers.

PERFORMANCE IN BATTLE

Electrical apparatus on shipboard was often subjected to strains far greater than those for which it was designed. Experiences similar to that of the cruiser U.S.S. *Houston* were by no means exceptional.

When the *Houston* was hit by Japanese torpedo bombers off Formosa, her main ship's service power supply was knocked out and the entire ship had to be operated on the power furnished by the emergency diesel generators. The maximum allowable load for the casualty power-supply cables was 65 amperes, but it was found necessary to step up the actual load to more than 100 amperes for periods as long as several hours. By this means it was possible to pump out the flooded compartments, to light the ship adequately, and to maintain essential communications. This situation continued for 13 days, but the power lines functioned without the slightest trouble. Their remarkable performance, according to the Navy, was a vital factor in keeping the ship afloat.

Equipment made by General Electric also played an important part in saving the U.S.S. *Hugh W. Hadley.* In a 90-minute action off Okinawa, in which she destroyed 23 Japanese planes, the *Hadley* was hit by two suicide aircraft, a Baka bomb, and an aerial bomb. Badly holed, listing heavily, her decks ablaze, both engine rooms flooded and one fire room flooded, the destroyer was in a desperate condition. But her emergency diesel-driven generators were workable, and they furnished power for the fire pumps and other damage-control machinery. This emergency power, together with the valiant efforts of the crew, saved the *Hadley.*

Durability of equipment in combat was demonstrated strikingly by H.M.S. *Essington* (DE-67), equipped with General Electric main propulsion controls, and brought special appreciation to the company from the British Admiralty. Operating east of the Azores in company with other British escort ships, aircraft of the Coastal Command and the United States Navy, the *Essington* helped beat off a desperate attack by a big U-boat force against a large Allied convoy. The battle lasted 4 days and 3 nights with only brief lulls. On the third day the *Essington* took the lead in stopping a strong force of enemy submarines moving in to attack the convoy from the flanks and rear. Depth charges from the DE blew one of the U-boats to the surface in a badly damaged condition. It remained visible for a few minutes and then disappeared. The entire convoy arrived at its destination practically unscathed.

"DOWN-THE-HATCH" WELDER

Making repairs by welding was a vitally important use of electricity on shipboard. This was an old story to the Navy long before World War II. Generally there were two 300-ampere welding sets on ships of cruiser size or smaller, and four sets on battleships and carriers. The majority of these sets were of General Electric manufacture. Each ship was equipped with a special wiring system to provide current for the welders.

Scarcely had the United States become an active participant in the war before the Navy was faced with serious problems of battle damage to its ships operating far away from their base ports. The light cruiser *Marblehead*, more fortunate than some of her partners in the Battle of the Java Sea in March, 1942, managed to limp home with her wounds hastily patched up by emergency welding.

Although it saved the *Marblehead*, the welding equipment then used by the Navy had many disadvantages. Chief of them was its being tied to a special wiring system. In the event of battle damage to some section of the system, welding might be impossible throughout a considerable part of the ship. The equipment itself weighed 4,000 pounds and was awkward to move. Then, too, the cost of providing a special system of wiring was very high—higher, in fact, than the cost of the welding equipment itself.

Recognizing the disadvantages of this arrangement, General Electric engineers in 1941 suggested the use of lightweight portable welders that could be plugged right in to the ship's regular power supply. Representatives of the company and the Bureau of Ships held a series of meetings to consider the matter, but it was not until the summer of the following year, after a number of heavy engagements with the Japanese in the Pacific, that the Navy became actively interested. An agreement was reached that some trial installations should be made of portable welding sets for use on shipboard.

The design developed for this purpose was a compact, self-contained 200-ampere unit 36 inches long, 16 inches wide, and 16 inches high, weighing 400 pounds for alternating-current operation and 450 pounds for direct-current operation. It was light enough to be moved easily from place to place aboard ship, and small enough to be passed through a hatch-way.

The first order, placed by the Navy in July, 1942, was for a trial lot of six sets. This was promptly increased to 50 machines and spare parts. They were built at the River Works, Lynn. At first they were delivered at a rate of five a week. Additional orders were received from time to time, and the rate of production was stepped up. Before the war was over, they were being turned out at a rate of 185 a week. Every ship in the Navy, from battleship to landing craft had received, or was scheduled to receive, one of these light-weight, "down-the-hatch" welding sets.

Shipboard welding proved its value on innumerable occasions, but never more dramatically than it did one day in the summer of 1944. The U.S.S. *Intrepid*, a 27,000-ton aircraft carrier, was in the thick of the fighting off the coast of Okinawa. All its planes were in the air when a Japanese suicide plane began a sudden dive for the ship. Before the antiaircraft guns could stop it, the Kamikaze hit the flight deck and plunged on through to the hangar deck, where its 1,200-pound bomb exploded with terrific force.

The hangar deck was badly battered, but the most serious feature of the damage was the gaping hole in the flight deck. The *Intrepid*'s planes were on the way home from their mission and would soon be coming in to land. Quick repair of the flight deck was a vital necessity so the planes could land before they ran out of gas. All the ship's welding equipment was pressed into service. A temporary steel patch, 15 feet long by 20 feet wide, was laid on and welded in the short space of 45 minutes. So rapidly was the job done that every plane was able to land safely on the ship. Again electricity had demonstrated its inestimable value on shipboard.

5

Repairs for Fighting Machinery

WHEN THE JAPANESE ATTACKED at Pearl Harbor on Dec. 7, 1941, they caught the major part of the United States fleet off balance. Americans were shocked as they had never been shocked before when they heard of the disaster. But they did not know the worst. For reasons of security they were told only that two battleships, the *Arizona* and the *Oklahoma,* and the old training ship *Utah* had been completely incapacitated, and that numerous other vessels had been damaged but could be restored to service.

That was true, but this hopeful official report was a masterpiece of understatement. The *Arizona* had blown up. The *Oklahoma* had capsized. The *Nevada* had been beached. The *California* and the *West Virginia* had sunk at their moorings. The *Tennessee* had burned, and the flagship *Pennsylvania* had been badly battered as she lay in dry dock. In short, each and every one of the seven battleships at the Pearl Harbor Naval Base had been put out of action for an indefinite period. Numerous smaller ships had been severely damaged, and a few destroyed. What was left of the United States fighting fleet in the Pacific was an aggregation of some aircraft carriers and a limited number of cruisers and destroyers.

47

Not until long afterward did the public—and the Japanese—learn the extent of the damage that had been inflicted. But the U.S. Navy knew and understood the tremendous task involved in restoring the damaged ships to service. The most acute problem was to reclaim the *California* and the *West Virginia,* two of the biggest and best of the Navy's battleships. Like the *New Mexico* and the huge aircraft carriers *Saratoga* and *Lexington,* they were equipped with turbine-electric drive made by the General Electric Company. Damaged heavily by the Japanese attack, they had settled to the bottom of the harbor with their decks awash.

WORK ON BATTLESHIPS AT PEARL HARBOR

A hurry call was sent to the company for men to help repair these vessels. Skilled armature winders, motor experts, and supervisors were summoned by telephone from all parts of the country. One of the company's most experienced erecting engineers was taken away from the job of installing generators at the Cherokee Dam to superintend the work at Pearl Harbor. The largest single group, 15 men from Schenectady, sped to the West Coast in a special Pullman car. Five men were borrowed from the Bureau of Power and Light in Los Angeles. Altogether a total of 58 men was assembled.

Never before had propulsion equipment of this size had to be repaired under such conditions. The men found the motors covered by thick oil and muck, some corroded by immersion in salt water. The electric-propulsion apparatus was deep in the hull of each ship, and everything had to be taken in or out by men walking single file on narrow companionways through four decks. Many tons of material were moved in this way.

The men worked in the holds in three shifts of 8 hours each, 7 days a week, breathing air pumped from abovedecks. As a precaution against gas, they wore chemically treated white ribbons. If the ribbons turned purple, the men had to leave immediately.

Working space was so cramped that special techniques had to be improvised. In repairing the huge 12-foot motors used to drive a battleship, the usual practice is to turn the machine over on its side so that the laminations can more easily be stacked and pressed into place. This was out of the question on the ships sunk at Pearl Harbor. Consequently, hundreds of thin sheets of metal laminations had to be laboriously stacked and pressed into place while the motor stood in normal operating position. A method of doing this was devised, which used hydraulic jacks exerting a pressure of 150 tons. The rotors of the motors had to be ground round to a running clearance of approximately one-tenth of an inch.

A special problem in replacement of material required the direction of an experienced engineer from the Induction Motor Division. He left Schenectady on Sunday afternoon, flying to San Francisco where he arrived on Monday. There a Clipper had been held 4 hours for him, and he continued immediately to Honolulu, arriving on Tuesday.

Work continued at top speed on the propulsion machinery of the big ships until once again they were able to move under their own power. "In recognition of the valuable services performed" by these men in the repair of the *California* and the *West Virginia*, the Commandant of the Pearl Harbor Navy Yard presented a Navy "E" pin to each man of the group.

REFLOATING THE U.S.S. *OKLAHOMA*

Salvage of the U.S.S. *Oklahoma* presented the Navy with a problem very different from those involved with the *California* and the *West Virginia*. The *Oklahoma* was a 30,000-ton battleship that had almost turned turtle and was lying with nothing but her keel and part of her bottom above water.

The first thing to be done, of course, was to get her right side up. Twenty-one giant, timber A frames were mounted along the bilge keel from bow to stern of the ship to provide leverage for the necessary turning movement. Compound pulleys were then set up for each frame so that the force exerted was multiplied many times.

This arrangement for righting a capsized ship dated back to the time of Archimedes. The famous Greek scientist applied it on a much smaller scale in the year 285 B.C. to right a 200-ton war galley belonging to the King of Syracuse. Slaves furnished the power, but the pull they exerted on the ropes was so increased by the compound pulley system that the ship was quickly righted.

At Pearl Harbor large cables reeved through the compound pulleys ran to 21 electric winches on the shore. It was imperative that the winch motors should respond precisely to individual control. Nobody could predict exactly what would happen when the huge vessel started to roll back to her normal position. The forces involved were tremendous, and failure to control them properly might result in breaking the ship apart. An operator was stationed at each winch to make quick changes in its speed, in order to equalize the strain on the turning ship.

To accomplish this job, variable-voltage drives were rounded up from General Electric factories and warehouses all over the country. These units were assembled at the company's San Francisco service shop where they were adapted for the particular task they were to perform. Control equipment had to be built from such parts as were immediately obtainable. The entire lot of equipment then had to be tested before being shipped to Honolulu.

When all this machinery was in position, the Navy began the delicate work of righting the ship. Slowly but steadily the list was decreased as the winches tugged on the cables. At the end of 72 hours of operation the vessel had been rotated to within 2½ degrees of its natural upright position, and the cables were slacked off. The *Oklahoma* was back "on her feet."

10,000 MILES IN SIX DAYS

Another type of rush repair job was common in the dark days following Pearl Harbor when the seaworthy vessels of the United States fleet were spread pretty thinly over the vast area of the Pacific Ocean. Every ship that could navigate and fire a gun was needed every instant. When one was damaged, immediate repair was essential.

At six o'clock on a Thursday afternoon in the spring of 1942 an urgent call for help came to General Electric's Schenectady Works. A Navy ship was lying crippled in a South Pacific port near Australia. She needed many repair parts and needed them desperately.

An executive hurriedly checked the list, reached for the telephone, and started calling key men from their homes to answer the ship's SOS. They jumped into their autos and raced down to the plant. Some of them worked all night. Some kept at it all the next day. They grabbed what they needed from production lines. They raided assembly lines. But, with it all, regular production never faltered.

By nightfall on Friday, the next day, the job had been completed. The stack of repair parts needed by the crippled vessel had been assembled in the shipping room. A shipping crew, working feverishly, packed 39 cases with the assembled material.

Naval authorities were notified. Clearance was received for transport by plane. Escorted by police, the cases were rushed to the airport and loaded. On Sunday morning they arrived in San Francisco. On Wednesday, 6 days after the request had been received, a bombing plane landed the equipment at its destination in the South Pacific, more than 10,000 miles from the factory where it originated.

SPEED RECORDS BROKEN

Again and again repair jobs on war equipment were handled in amazingly quick time. Once a British man-of-war docked at the Charlestown Navy Yard with a badly damaged armature on a 175-kilowatt generator. The armature was removed and rushed to the River Works at Lynn, where it arrived late on Saturday night. Instructions were that repairs must be completed within a week, though the job would normally take from 2 to 3 weeks.

Men were on the job at daybreak Sunday. They worked continuously, with meals brought in to them, and with barely enough time off for sleep. The armature was disassembled, the copper coils retaped, and put back in place. Then the reassembled machine was carefully tested. On Friday it was back again at the Charlestown Navy Yard.

On another Saturday, General Electric's New York service shop received a rush call from the Navy to fix one 50-horsepower and one 24-horsepower motor that had been submerged in oil for several days. Thursday was set as the deadline for completion of the task. Work started immediately and continued on a 24-hour basis until the job was finished. Coils were removed, cleaned, baked, tested, and reinstalled. Spare coils were made up and held in readiness, but none was needed. By Tuesday the task was done and the equipment returned for installation in the vessel, 2 days ahead of the Navy's deadline.

Not weeks or days, but hours and minutes, measured the speed of one repair job. A submarine docked one day at a Pacific coast port with one of the ship's motor-field controllers needing replacement. A telephone call for a new unit was received at the Erie Works at eight o'clock in the morning. The motor-field controller required was a complicated piece of equipment for regulating the speed of the main propulsion motors of the submarine. To put one together would

Task Force 58 on the move to strike a Japanese stronghold. This was the most powerful and destructive unit in the history of naval warfare.

Tanker refueling U.S. aircraft carrier at sea. Their high speed enabled these tankers to keep up with fleet movements.

SS Mission Purisima—a fast new tanker built during the war. G.E. supplied turbine-electric drive for 378 ships of this general type.

Compact but powerful—10,000-horsepower turbine generator set in the engine room of the SS Mission Purisima.

*Ships behind the headlines—some of the thousands of cargo ves-
sels which transported and maintained the greatest waterborne
invading force in history.*

Final assembly of ship propulsion turbine-gear set at the River Works. High pressure turbine rotor being lowered into place.

Maritime Commissions type C-2 cargo vessel equipped with G-E 6000-horsepower turbine-gear drive, was designed for peacetime as well as wartime use.

Swinging high in air from two revolving cranes, a large ship propulsion motor waits to be lowered into the hull of a tanker.

Powerful deep-sea tug for salvage operations, equipped with G-E generators and motors developing 3000 horsepower.

Diesel-electric drive net tender for laying and tending submarine nets at harbor entrances and fleet anchorages.

Most of the newer submarines of the U.S. Navy such as this 1500-ton vessel, have diesel-electric drive.

Much complex equipment is packed into the control room of a submarine.

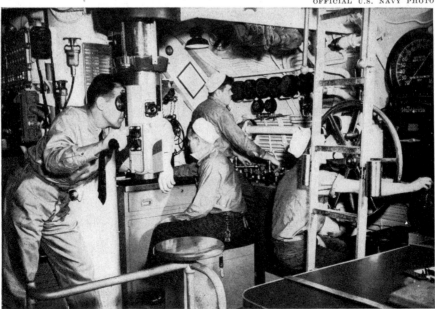

Building auxiliary generators at Fitchburg Works to provide ship's service power

Anchor windlass—one of the dozens of uses of shipboard electric power.

Electric motor for operating lifeboat winch on cargo ship.

Floodlights turn night into day as precious war cargo is unloaded in a European port.

Battle formation on the signal bridge of a U.S. warship. Signalling searchlight at left.

Ice cream freezer aboard a U.S. destroyer provides a
"home-town drug store" touch.

This factory-assembled refrigeration unit saved
space on cargo ships.

U.S.S. California sinking into the mud at Pearl Harbor after Japanese attack.

Rescuing sailors from the U.S.S. West Virginia as the ship burned on December 7, 1941.

U.S.S. West Virginia on the bottom at Pearl Harbor with her turbine-electric equipment completely submerged.

On the way to drydock for repairs—the U.S.S. West Virginia after being raised.

Bottomside up at Pearl Harbor—salvage gear mounted along keel of U.S.S. Oklahoma.

Cables rigged from these timber frames when drawn by winches on shore gradually righted the capsized battleship.

ordinarily take about 20 hours. Men were quickly at work assembling the new unit. Parts were borrowed from three different kinds of controllers then in production at the plant. A total of some ninety different soldering operations were involved in making the electrical connections.

Everyone worked at top speed. By 2:30 P.M. that same day the new controller had been assembled. A half hour later it was in the shipping department being boxed for shipment by air express to the Pacific Coast. A 20-hour job had been successfully completed in the record time of only 5½ hours.

FLOATING "SICK BAYS" FOR SHIPS

Among the many unusual naval developments of the war was the use of floating dry docks. Formerly, a crippled vessel had to limp from the scene of battle damage all the way back to the nearest land-base dry dock for any major repairs that might be necessary. This was often hundreds of miles from the battle area.

From time to time the U.S. Navy had experimented with floating dry docks that could be moved from place to place as occasion might demand. These experiments had met with very limited success. The plan worked well enough for small docks, but those of larger size proved extremely unwieldy in transit. Their long, high sides presented too great an expanse in the path of ocean gales. When attempts were made to tow them, they broke loose from their tugs, cracked apart, and sometimes even capsized.

At the beginning of World War II the United States Navy, in general, held a very low opinion of the value of floating dry docks for large ships. Permanent dry-dock facilities were available at Pearl Harbor and in the Philippines. The British had a large dock at Singapore. Others were located in the Dutch East Indies. With these facilities available, there seemed little need for additional dry docks.

The outbreak of hostilities in the Pacific, however, changed the picture with remarkable rapidity. Facilities at Pearl Harbor were badly damaged by the initial Japanese attack. Then the Philippines, Singapore, and the Dutch East Indies were lost. There were no large dry docks left nearer than the West Coast of the United States mainland.

Even before this happened, Rear Admiral F. R. Harris, retired, a former Chief of the Navy's Bureau of Yards and Docks, had been urging the construction of a new type of floating dry dock. He had been in charge during some of the earlier, unsuccessful experiments with floating dry docks and believed that he had a way of overcoming the difficulties that had been encountered at that time. His plan was to build the dock in sections with collapsible side walls. In this way a large structure could be moved in small pieces, with the walls flat on the deck and offering little resistance to the wind.

The Navy Department gave him permission to go ahead with the construction of a number of docks of this kind, provided that they could be built in shipyards that were not doing important work for the Navy, and provided also that no material or equipment was used that might be needed for other purposes.

These restrictions were a considerable obstacle, but Admiral Harris went ahead anyway. The basis of the new design was a standard steel section, not unlike the hull of a ship with a flat deck, completely equipped and suitable for individual transportation. After arrival at their destination, the sections could be assembled side by side into dry docks of any desired length, up to that required for the largest vessel afloat.

Each section was a kind of seagoing barge, 256 feet long and 80 feet wide. The deck was nearly rectangular, but the bow and stern were tapered at the water line for ease in towing. This barge carried two sections of wing wall, one for each side of the dock. Wing walls were 33 feet thick and 56 feet high. They were hinged to the deck of the barge and were raised by jacks when the dock was being assembled. A distance of 140 feet separated the insides of the wing walls when they had been raised.

ENOUGH ELECTRIC EQUIPMENT FOR A FACTORY

At the two ends of the section were huge ballast tanks for submerging and raising the dock. Amidship were living quarters for a crew of forty men and space for a vast array of machinery. As the sections had to be sunk well below the surface of the water to permit a ship to enter the dock, they had no portholes. Each section was artificially ventilated and lighted, and provided with electric ranges for cooking and electric refrigeration for food storage. A hatch in the deck and one in the underside of the raised wing wall were joined in a watertight connection to permit men to enter and leave the hull when the section was submerged. Air ducts for ventilation also passed through this connection to a point high up in the wing wall well above water level at all times.

Enough electric equipment to operate a moderate-sized factory was installed on each barge. Two 350-kilowatt generators driven by diesel engines provided the necessary power. These generators were tied together to provide a total of 7,000 kilowatts of power for a ten-section dock. Electrically operated pumps were used for emptying the ballast tanks when the barge was to be raised. Other large pumps were provided for fire fighting in case a ship was docked with a fire burning in her hold. Each section was provided with heavy anchors and chains. Anchor windlasses at bow and stern were electrically operated. On the top of each wing wall was a 30-ton electric jib crane. Loudspeakers were installed throughout to permit the docking officer to control every phase of the intricate process of docking a large vessel. Brilliant floodlights permitted repair work on a damaged ship to be pushed day and night without interruption. These various services demanded a large supply of electric power. In addition, it was necessary to supply the power needed for lights, ventilation, communication, and a host of other purposes on the ships docked for repairs.

In accordance with the Navy's stipulation about not interfering with other work, Admiral Harris turned to the smaller shipyards, mostly inland, for the construction of the floating dry docks. Interchangeable sections were built hundreds of miles from salt water—far up the Mississippi, Missouri, and Ohio rivers—and floated down to the Gulf of Mexico. For generators, pump motors, and similar equipment he turned to General Electric. Again following the Navy's instructions, the company supplied standard industrial electrical equipment of types not being used for other purposes by the Navy or Army—switchgear from Philadelphia, generators from Schenectady, motors from Lynn, Schenectady, and Oakland, transformers, reactors, and other equipment from Pittsfield.

It took about 6 months to build the first lot of sections. Each section was towed separately across the ocean by a Liberty ship to a sheltered, deepwater harbor in the Southwest Pacific. The trip was not an easy one. Despite their tapered bows and sterns, the sections could not be towed faster than 6 knots. Life for the crew was a good deal like living on a submarine as there was little deck space on the barges and what there was could not be used in stormy weather.

Altogether it took about 2 months to get all the sections to their destination. Then began the job of assembling them into a complete dry dock. The first section was brought into position and firmly anchored. Wing walls were raised. The second section was brought alongside and locked to the first. The two sections were then welded together. This process was continued until a total of ten sections had been assembled. The completed dock had a surface as long as three football fields with side walls rising higher than a five-story building.

Two months were required for the job of assembling the dock. It was completed in the summer of 1943. Immediately it was put to work repairing an accumulation of damaged ships that had been lying idle in various harbors in the Southwest Pacific. The procedure in docking a ship was to admit water into the ballast compartments of the dock until it was submerged to a depth of some 50 feet, leaving the tops of the wing walls only about 5 feet out of water. The ship to be repaired was then towed into the dock and made fast to the wing walls. This done, the water was pumped out of the ballast chambers and the resulting buoyancy raised the ship until the deck of the dock was about 2 feet out of water. This was an extremely complicated process involving the most precise control, as the weight of the ship was unevenly distributed among the various sections, and unwatering of the compartments had to proceed at different rates so that the ship would remain horizontal.

The success of the first of these docks was so pronounced that the program was at once extended to include three 10-section docks for battleships or large aircraft carriers, and five 7-section docks for cruisers and other ships of moderate size. Later, five more of these sectional floating dry docks were ordered by the Navy but they were not completed in time to see actual service during the war.

Whereas the old concept of sea strategy required ships to operate within an approximate range of 2,000 miles from a permanent repair base, the floating dry docks made it possible to establish bases where they were needed and to plan operations anywhere in the entire Pacific. Places where they were located included the Admiralty Isles, Iwo Jima, Leyte, Alaska, Okinawa, and the Philippine Islands.

In a single year these floating repair shops handled more than 200 battle-damaged ships. Largest of them was the 32,-000-ton battleship *Tennessee*, with serious torpedo wounds in her hull. Though more than 600 feet long and 100 feet broad, she fitted into the dock with considerable room to spare.

These docks served to repair a good many ships that would probably not have survived the trip to the nearest land base. At Okinawa the cruiser *Philadelphia* had her entire bow torn off and was left with only one bulkhead preserving buoyancy enough to keep her afloat. To have undertaken a trip to the mainland of the United States would have been fatal to a ship in her condition. In the floating dry dock she was completely repaired and returned to service in less time than it would have taken her to reach the nearest base, if she could have reached that haven at all.

At the conclusion of the war Admiral Harris wrote a letter to General Electric stating that the quality of the company's machines and its cooperation in supplying them promptly had "contributed greatly to the successful operation of these docks and the winning of the war in the Pacific."

6

Pattern of Invasion

EVERY MAJOR WAR has brought out at least one important
new weapon. In World War II, one of the big surprises was
that incredible contrivance, the landing craft. Built in a wide
variety of shapes and sizes, landing craft provided an ideal
answer to one of war's oldest and toughest problems—how
to start a successful invasion on a hostile coast.

BIRTH OF A NEW WEAPON

The idea was born out of the tragic experience of Dunkerque. After the unexpected surrender of the Belgian Army
the British Expeditionary Force had to extricate itself as
best it could through the only port not in enemy hands.
Dunkerque alone remained open, and its facilities were piti-
fully inadequate for the movement of hundreds of thousands
of men.

The Germans were confident that they had the British in
a trap from which there could be no escape. But they reck-
oned without British gameness. Hurriedly the call went out
to mobilize virtually everything that would float, wherever
it might be in the British Isles—trawlers, yachts, motorboats,
tugs, excursion steamers, and other craft of every description.

This strange armada was dispatched to Dunkerque. Then the Tommies on the beaches waded into the sea, boarded this motley fleet, and were ferried home. Three-quarters of the Expeditionary Force, along with some French, Belgians, and Dutch, were saved in this most spectacular rescue in naval history.

Winston Churchill grimly remarked that "Wars are not won by evacuations." Nevertheless, Dunkerque taught a lesson that played a vital part in winning the war. It showed that harbors and docks for big ships are not essential for embarking or disembarking masses of men in wartime. It can be done, if necessary, over open beaches with small boats.

AMERICA'S ALPHABET NAVY

Hitler's seizure of all of Western Europe meant that no ports would be available for the invasion of the Continent. Some sort of small boats must be provided by which men and equipment could be landed right on the beaches.

Before the British had proceeded very far in the development of landing craft, the United States had entered the war, and the need for vessels of this type was greatly increased. Then began the creation of America's remarkable "Alphabet Navy."

Three general types of equipment were developed—landing vehicles, landing craft, and landing ships. In the first category were the motorized amphibious "Alligators," "Water Buffalos," and "Ducks." The second class included the LCR (landing craft, rubber), LCP (landing craft, personnel), LCV (landing craft, vehicle), LCT (landing craft, tank), and a number of others. The third category included the LSI (landing ship, infantry), LSM (landing ship, medium), and LST (landing ship, tank).

Largest of these, the LST had a length of 330 feet, a beam of 50 feet, and displacement of 3,000 tons. She could carry thirty to forty tanks on her two decks, or a substantially larger number of jeeps or trucks. In some instances standard railroad trains were transported from England to France aboard LST's.

The requirements for these ships were enough to drive the design engineers frantic. Although long range was demanded, there was little space that could be spared for engines and fuel storage. Shallow draft was essential in order to get the ships well inshore for landing operations, but also these ships had to be able to cross the ocean without capsizing.

At the bow were huge doors which swung outward and a cleated ramp which was lowered to permit the tanks to drive off the ship onto the beach. The sides of the vessel were lined with tanks for fuel oil and ballast. The ballast tanks provided not only stability at sea, but also the necessary trim to get the ship off the beach after unloading. A stern anchor dropped as the ship approached the shore aided in that operation. When she was ready to depart, a power windlass hauled in the anchor chain and helped her draw herself off the beach. Electric motors were used for the operation of doors, ramps, fuel pumps, ballast pumps, and windlasses, and for a variety of other purposes.

EXPANSION OF LST PROGRAM

The Navy's initial LST program, undertaken early in 1942, comprised 300 vessels. In April of that year, General Electric's River Works at Lynn received orders for 5,100 electric motors to be delivered at a rate of 510 per month. In May the company received orders for 4,850 more motors to equip an additional 190 vessels.

The first test of the LST's came on November 8, when landings were made at Algiers and Oran on the north coast of Africa and at Casablanca on the west coast. This test was a complete success.

It had been expected that the Germans would be driven

out of North Africa in a month, and that a cross-channel invasion could be started sometime in 1943, but the North African campaign proved to be tougher than had been expected and the cross-channel invasion of the Continent had to be postponed. It took all of the summer of 1943 to mop up Africa, to capture Sicily, and to establish the Allied armies firmly in Italy.

At a meeting of President Roosevelt, Prime Minister Churchill, and their advisers at Quebec in September it was decided to undertake the cross-channel invasion of France in the spring of 1944. Since this operation was to involve nearly three times as many troops as the campaign in the Mediterranean, additional landing vessels would be needed in quantity.

During September, October, and November, General Electric received orders for approximately 3,000 motors for some 200 additional LST's. Even this was insufficient. General Eisenhower decided that the initial cross-channel assault force should be increased from three divisions to five, and still more landing vessels were needed.

OVERRIDING PRIORITY FOR INVASION CRAFT

According to an Associated Press dispatch from Washington at that time, "Invasion craft have been put ahead of everything else in the nation's arsenal, with the granting of an overriding priority giving them the right of way over planes, high-octane gasoline, and all other urgency product programs."

For this extra-rush program, General Electric was assigned the job of building some 10,000 additional motors. On top of previous orders, this made a cumulative total, including battle-damage spares, of 30,000 motors, representing about 300,000 horsepower.

Everything possible was done to meet these tremendous schedules. At the River Works thousands of other jobs were reshuffled to speed up LST motor production. This proved to be a complicated undertaking. Every unit in the process of manufacture at the time had to be checked to see if it was even remotely hampering the LST program. When this was found to be so, permission was sought from the War Production Board to change the schedule. All materials and all work in process had to be physically removed from the manufacturing floor to make room for LST units.

The production battle continued grimly through the winter and spring months. Then came the great day in Normandy. The infantry swam and waded ashore from the largest fleet of warcraft that had ever been assembled. Behind the smaller landing craft came the "big boys." Like giant whales the LST's slid up to the newly gained beaches. Their cavernous jaws opened and out rolled the tanks that were destined to bang their way right into the heart of Germany, so that 11 months later General Eisenhower could send the Combined Chiefs of Staff the laconic message from Reims, "The mission of this Allied Force was fulfilled at 0241 local time, May 7, 1945."

MAGNETIC-MINE DEFENSE

A little known but vitally important part of all invasion operations was mine sweeping. Before the ships of an invasion armada could leave their home ports, the navigation channels had to be cleared of mines. Before the ships could land at the invasion beaches or ports, the danger of mines had to be eliminated.

Mine sweeping in World War II demanded a technique different from any used in previous wars. The general idea of mining the waters adjacent to harbors was old and had often been used in earlier wars, but the type of mines was new. Previous practice had been to anchor the mines just below the surface of the water where they could not be seen by the ships' lookouts, but would be exploded if struck by the hull of a passing ship. The most widely used method of mine sweeping in World War I involved the use of a dragline between two vessels to cut the mines loose from their anchors so that they would rise to the surface of the water where they could be exploded by gunfire.

The great difficulty in laying these contact mines was that the operation required an extremely accurate knowledge of the depth of water in the areas to be mined and extremely exact anchoring of the mines so that they would be deep enough to be invisible but not so deep that ships would pass over without striking them. To avoid these difficulties magnetic mines were developed as substitutes for the older types. Instead of being anchored between the surface of the water and the bottom and being exploded by contact, the magnetic mines were placed directly on the bottom and exploded by the magnetic effect of a steel ship passing above them. This made mine laying a great deal simpler and mine sweeping a great deal more complicated.

Both Britain and the United States had developed magnetic mines a good while before World War II began, but they had not developed any successful means of combatting magnetic mines laid by the enemy. Scarcely had the war begun when the Germans set to work laying magnetic mines in the waters around the British Isles. After the fall of France the Nazis mined all the harbors along the French coast. Later they extended their operations to harbors along the Atlantic seaboard of the United States.

Intensive efforts to combat magnetic mines were undertaken by the U.S. Navy as soon as the war started. These followed two general lines: (1) exploding the mines harmlessly as soon as they were laid and before they had a chance to blow up a ship, and (2) demagnetizing ships so that they could pass over the mines without detonating them.

The method of exploding the mines deliberately involved setting up an artificial disturbance of the earth's magnetic field similar to that which might be caused by the presence of a steel ship. This was accomplished at first by towing barges back and forth, equipped with large permanent magnets or electromagnets. Such procedure was effective from the standpoint of exploding the mines artificially, but was rather expensive because the equipment creating the magnetic disturbance was located right in the barges and the mines were often exploded with the barges directly above them, resulting in the destruction of a good many barges.

Experiments by the British showed that it was possible to create the desired magnetic disturbance by trailing an electric cable behind a pair of ships and passing electric current through the cable. An improvement on this method was the use of a pair of cables of different lengths trailing behind a single ship, the current passing through the water from the end of one cable to the end of the other. Storage batteries furnished the current. Since the magnetic mines were sensitive to polarity, it was necessary to set up disturbances of the earth's magnetic field in both directions. Circuit breakers with mechanical timing devices were used to switch the flow of current back and forth through the water.

All the U.S. Navy's mine sweepers had diesel engines, some with mechanical drive for the propellers and some with electric drive. Equipment on about eighty twin-screw vessels of the latter type included four 700-kilowatt generators. Since only two of these were ordinarily required for propulsion, the other two were available to supply current for the magnetic-mine detonating cables. Ships with diesel-mechanical drive were provided with auxiliary 500-kilowatt generators to serve the same purpose. General Electric built more than 600 of these generators, which provided a power supply greatly superior to that previously obtained from storage batteries.

In mine-sweeping operations over sizable areas it was customary for several ships to work together, two or three abreast, sweeping in parallel lines. This required that the changes of polarity of the several equipments be synchronized, so that the ships would supplement rather than neutralize each other. Various electrical manufacturers were asked by the Navy to design timing devices for this purpose. General Electric began work on the project and quickly developed an underwater electric signal system to synchronize the generators. The first production unit was ready for shipment late in 1940, less than 2 months after receiving the Navy's request. These functioned with remarkable efficiency. Though later designs embodied minor modifications, the basic principles were the same. By the early part of 1945 the company had turned out a total of more than 800 units and was the sole producer of this equipment.

Greatest of all the war's mine-sweeping jobs was that of clearing the way for the huge armada that crossed the English Channel to land on the coast of Normandy on D Day. Thousands of ships of every description had assembled in the harbors of Britain. The entrances to these harbors had to be swept clear before the invasion armada could leave port. Then a broad path across the channel had to be cleared. Finally the French coast had to be made safe. Mine sweepers of the American and British navies worked together on this job. Since the English Channel and both the English and French coasts presented many favorable locations for laying magnetic mines either by airplane or submarine, the work of the mine sweepers continued without ceasing until the close of the war.

This, however, was only one of the important mine-sweeping jobs of the American Navy. The great ports along the Atlantic seacoast of the United States had to be kept clear, too. Mine laying around these ports was more difficult for the Germans because the distance from their bases was too great for airplanes to operate, but numerous submarines crossed the ocean, and mines were discovered from time to time outside a number of American harbors.

In the Pacific the Navy had the job of mine sweeping outside the ports on the west coast of the United States and at Pearl Harbor. Even more important was the job of sweeping the approaches to the Japanese-held islands, as the Pacific campaign proceeded step by step on the road to Tokyo. So effective were the Navy's mine-sweeping technique and equipment that the great invasion campaigns against both the Germans and the Japanese were able to proceed with only infinitesimal losses from enemy mines.

DEGAUSSING MEASUREMENTS

A second means of defense against magnetic mines was to demagnetize the ships traveling in areas where they were likely to encounter magnetic mines. This process was called degaussing from the word "gauss," a measure of magnetic flux density. By wrapping several turns of wire around the hull of a ship and passing electric current through the wire it was possible to neutralize the effect of the earth's magnetic field on the metal hull of the ship and the electric equipment inside the hull. Virtually every ship that traveled in dangerous waters had degaussing equipment. High-current, low-voltage motor-generator sets for this purpose were built at River Works.

Before a ship could be degaussed, however, it was necessary first to secure data concerning the ship's magnetic characteristics. In response to a request from the Navy, G.E.'s General Engineering Laboratory developed a special fluxmeter for this purpose. These instruments were set up at some convenient location and connected to coils on the harbor bottom. Ships to be degaussed were passed over them. From the fluxmeter readings the effect of the ship on a magnetic mine could be quickly determined. If the ship had not been degaussed sufficiently to be safe, corrective measures were taken. The ship was then passed and repassed over the "range" until pronounced satisfactory.

A total of 2,400 of these fluxmeters was built by the company. Their use in measuring the magnetic effect of a ship was a rather time-consuming process, however, and a magnetometer was later developed to measure the magnetic field of a ship at rest. General Electric produced several thousand of these instruments to speed up degaussing measurements.

By having a fluxmeter installation just inside the entrance to a harbor it was a simple matter to check the degaussing adjustment of every ship entering or leaving. If the adjustment was satisfactory, there was no delay; but if it was not, the ship was told to take remedial measures, the effect of which could then be measured at the same location or by magnetometer if that was more convenient.

Some of the old-time skippers thought the whole degaussing procedure was nonsense. The story is told that one skeptical captain turned off the electric current from his degaussing cables shortly after he had passed over the fluxmeter cables and received his signal to proceed out of the harbor. Within a minute after the degaussing mechanism ceased to function his ship was blown in two by a magnetic mine.

Although the fluxmeter was first developed in connection with the defense against magnetic mines, it was used also for defense against enemy submarines. In this use a supersensitive instrument was energized by a loop of cables laid entirely across the bottom of a harbor entrance or other narrow body of water. When a ship crossed the loop, small voltages were induced in the cables by the changes in the earth's magnetic field, even though the ship was sufficiently degaussed to be safe from magnetic mines. The device was so sensitive that it registered the passage of a vessel as small as a motorboat, due to the presence of iron in the ship. An observer stationed beside a fluxmeter on shore could thus de-

*G-E service shop men repairing a propulsion motor in the hold of
a cargo vessel.*

Section of Navy floating drydock with side walls lowered being towed to a forward area in the Pacific.

End view of floating drydock assembled with side walls raised.

*Repairing 32,000-ton battleship Tennessee in a floating drydock
set up in a quiet harbor in the far Pacific.*

Work continued at night under brilliant floodlights to hasten repairs to battle-damaged warships.

Embarking for the great invasion—equipment being loaded on LST's at a British port.

*Largest of the various types of landing craft was the 330-foot LST.
General Electric supplied 300,000 horsepower of motors for these
vessels.*

*Fighters pour down the ramp from a landing craft, infantry onto
a Normandy beach as bullets whizz overhead.*

With decks closely packed with men and motorized fighting equipment, LST's move toward a hostile shore.

U.S. landing ship, tank, starts unloading operations as a couple of trucks roll down onto the beach.

*Fast mine-layer at work—mines are rolled along tracks at sides
of ship and dropped off stern.*

Supported by its parachute a magnetic mine drifts slowly downward toward the surface of the water.

Magnetic mines provided with parachutes being dropped.

Submarine launching a magnetic mine.

Loading magnetic mines in a B-29.

*Dangerous work rewarded by success—a magnetic mine harm-
lessly exploded by U.S. Navy minesweepers.*

Twin screw diesel-electric drive mine-sweeper equipped with
General Electric generators, motors and control.

Formation of mine sweepers clearing a channel.

*Where fluxmeter records were interpreted to determine adjust-
ments necessary in ships' degaussing gear to give protection
against magnetic mines.*

*Supersensitive fluxmeters indicate passage of ships
through harbor entrance by ups and downs on charts.*

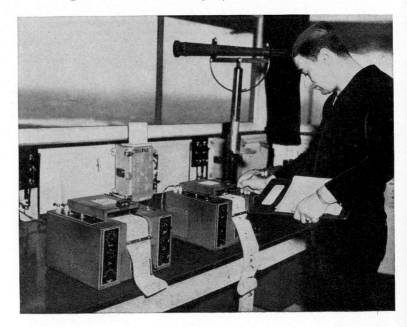

tect the passage of any vessel moving in the waters of a harbor entrance even though the vessel was completely hidden from the human eye.

When the supersensitive fluxmeter was first developed, a special demonstration was arranged one night at an Atlantic port for high-ranking officers of the U.S. Navy. The plan was to connect the apparatus, allow considerable time to elapse while the fluxmeter indicator stood stationary, and then send an unseen boat through the harbor entrance to demonstrate the ability of the fluxmeter to detect its passage. Everything started as planned. The apparatus was installed. The high-ranking officers were assembled. The operation of the instrument was explained. The switch was closed, making the electric connection, and the period of waiting began. But, instead of remaining quietly at rest until the prearranged ship passage took place, the indicator of the fluxmeter immediately began a slow steady swing to one side. Then it came slowly back to normal and began to swing to the other side, exactly as it was supposed to do to indicate the passage of a ship. The naval officers looked puzzled and skeptical. The engineer in charge of the demonstration watched the movement of the indicator with horrified eyes. Was his instrument, so carefully designed and built, going crazy on the first trial? Communication was quickly established with the ships guarding the harbor entrance. What had happened to the demonstration ship? It was there waiting for its scheduled time to enter the harbor. Had anything else entered? Oh, yes, a tug had unexpectedly appeared and been passed into the harbor.

Fluxmeter installations of this kind were made at the entrance to every important harbor in the United States. Watch was kept 24 hours a day. Alongside the instrument was an alarm signal. Every time the fluxmeter indicated the passage of a ship, the watch sent the alarm to the control post. The latter was kept advised of authorized ship movement in the channel. So long as the fluxmeter warnings coincided with authorized movements, all was well. When an unauthorized movement was recorded, things began to happen fast. Harbor forts were alerted. Search planes took to the air. Speedy PT boats put out from near-by naval bases. All ordinary shipping was halted.

Many times, undoubtedly, the giving of the alarm turned out to have been unnecessary, having been occasioned by a vessel that meant no harm. But the Navy has never told the stories of these alarms, and no one will ever know exactly how many enemy attempts to enter harbors and destroy shipping were foiled by prompt responses to fluxmeter alarms.

7

Propulsion for Aircraft

In the air as well as at sea, General Electric equipment was a dominant factor in giving the armed forces of the United States superiority over their enemies. This was demonstrated in convincing fashion when, in the fall of 1942, American bombers made the first large-scale daylight raid on Hitler's "Fortress of Europe." One hundred and fifteen Flying Fortresses and Liberators, accompanied by a tremendous fighter escort, rose from the airfields of Britain and headed for the French coast. Hardly had they crossed the Channel when they were attacked by wave after wave of Focke-Wulfe and Messerschmitt fighters. After the battle was over and the final score was added up, the steel works at Lille had been left in flames and at least forty-eight German fighters had been knocked out of the sky. All but four of the U.S. bombers returned safely to their bases.

The big bombers had done what the men who built them and the men who flew them had always said they could do —fight through in broad daylight to their targets, bomb accurately from high altitudes, and return safely to their bases. Their effectiveness was due to a combination of heavy armament, a precision bombsight, and the turbosupercharger, which enabled them to fly at high altitudes where antiair-

71

craft fire was thin and intercepting fighters were at a disadvantage.

Aircraft engines, like crews, require extra oxygen at high altitudes, where the air is thinner than it is near the earth's surface. At an altitude of 30,000 feet, for example, an ordinary engine has only about one-quarter of its normal power. The most effective means to prevent this loss of power is a turbosupercharger.

In the operation of the turbosupercharger, exhaust gases from the plane's engine are directed against a series of buckets welded to the rim of a wheel. This wheel rotates at speeds up to 25,000 revolutions per minute. Mounted on the same shaft is a second wheel, which has radial vanes. These rotate inside a specially shaped casing, thus forming an air compressor. This compresses "thin" air to air at sea-level pressure and feeds it to the carburetor of the engine, thus maintaining constant fuel mixture and horsepower. By this means the full power of an airplane engine can be sustained at altitudes up to 34,000 feet. So essential were these devices that the Army Air Forces specified them for all big bombers and many smaller fighting craft.

DEVELOPMENT OF THE TURBOSUPERCHARGER

The story of the turbosupercharger is one of cooperation, genius, and plain hard work. There is an element of luck in the story, too, but the main piece of good fortune is that which brought 40 years of research and development on this device to a successful culmination at that precise hour in history at which it could exert maximum effect.

In 1900, Sanford A. Moss received the degree of Master of Science from the University of California for his work in connection with gas turbines. Then he went to work with the General Electric Company as a draftsman on internal-combustion engines. Cornell University gave Moss the degree of Doctor of Philosophy in 1903 for his thesis on gas turbines.

In the fall of that year General Electric, as part of its research work in gas turbines, began the development of a centrifugal compressor, and Doctor Moss became closely associated with that undertaking.

During World War I, General Electric built the first gear-driven supercharger in the United States. This was an air compressor driven from the engine through a system of gears. While it was able to render a useful service in providing additional air for combustion in the engine's cylinders, it had the disadvantage that it subtracted from the power available for the propeller.

In the same year the company also built the first turbine-driven supercharger, or turbosupercharger. Driven by the exhaust gases of the engine instead of being connected to the shaft, it did not deprive the propeller of any power whatsoever. It was first installed on a Liberty engine, which, before the installation of the turbosupercharger, developed 350 horsepower at sea level. Then it was taken to the top of Pike's Peak in Colorado—an elevation of 14,000 feet. There the engine without supercharger developed only 230 horsepower, a loss of about one-third. A turbosupercharger was installed and the engine tested again. This time it delivered 356 horsepower—six more than could be obtained at sea level without the turbosupercharger.

This development came too late for the "turbo" to become a factor in World War I. The armistice of November 11, 1918, brought an end to much of the design and production work on military aircraft. Experimentation continued with turbosuperchargers, but production dwindled to a mere trickle. In 1938, for example, the company built only fifteen.

Serious technical difficulties had to be overcome before the essentially simple turbosupercharger became really effective. How could a small piece of mechanical equipment withstand the strains caused by extreme differences in temperature—heat of 1,500 degrees Fahrenheit for exhaust gases inside the device and outside air for compression at 70 degrees below zero at high altitudes? Of what metal could the turbine buckets be made to withstand such high temperatures while rotating with a rim speed faster than a bullet travels? Lubrication of bearings and air pulsations in the compressor chamber posed additional problems.

EXPEDITING MANUFACTURE

At the outbreak of World War II, General Electric engineers were satisfied that metallurgical and engineering problems had been solved to an extent that would permit mass production of turbosuperchargers in place of early hand methods. The war was the starting signal for a wild race between Germany and the Allied Nations to give their respective planes the highest possible "ceiling." This race soon narrowed into a contest of methods for supercharging the engine. The demand for turbosuperchargers increased rapidly. After Pearl Harbor it skyrocketed.

The company's tiny supercharger factory at Lynn gave way to a large factory there. Then a new plant was built at near-by Everett, Mass., covering several acres of ground. Every possible step was taken to speed up its construction. Only a little more than 6 months elapsed between the drawing of the plans and the start of manufacture. By coincidence, ground was broken on the day before Pearl Harbor for a new, $25,000,000 turbosupercharger plant at Fort Wayne, Ind.

Ultimately, the making of turbosuperchargers occupied more than 1,500,000 square feet of floor space in the company's plants. Nearly 9,000 employees, most of them new, were engaged in this work. Still the turbosuperchargers were not being built fast enough to meet the nation's war needs. So the company turned over its designs and explained its manufacturing methods to two other companies having the necessary equipment for this work. To them it also loaned some of its engineers and supervisors to organize the start of operations in these outside plants.

One of the troublesome production bottlenecks was buckets. Originally these buckets were forged and machined. It became clear, however, that this method of manufacturing was too slow to meet the combined requirements of the three companies building the turbosuperchargers. An entirely new method was then developed of making buckets by casting them from Vitallium, an alloy used in making dental plates.

Two manufacturers expert in dental casting helped General Electric in this development. These concerns, following successful initial experiments, expanded their facilities and furnished complete buckets to all three turbosupercharger producers. By 1942 the old method of making buckets had been largely superseded.

FIRST VICTIM OF THE AAF

An American plane equipped with a turbosupercharger scored the first kill of an enemy plane. High above the dreary wastes of Iceland one morning 8 months after Pearl Harbor an American P-38 Lightning shot down a big German Focke-Wulfe. In itself this victory did not greatly affect the course of the war. Its significance lay in the fact that this was the first Nazi plane shot down by the U.S. Air Forces in the European theater of war. It also demonstrated the capabilities of the P-38.

Heaviest of all U.S. fighter planes, the P-38 was also one of the fastest. It was designed in 1936 and set an unofficial cross-continent record in 1939 by flying from March Field, Calif., to Mitchell Field, N.Y., in 7 hours and 20 minutes. Over Pittsburgh the pilot radioed his altitude as 22,000 feet and speed as 420 miles an hour. The Pittsburgh radio operator had taken reports from hundreds of passing planes, but he had never heard of such speed. He started to check back, but before he could finish his conversation the plane was out of radio range.

P-38's were the first American fighter planes to be flown nonstop across the Atlantic Ocean. Time and again they proved their worth in Europe and in the Pacific. They could climb faster, fly at greater altitudes and greater speed, and had heavier firepower than the enemy's fighters. In large measure this was attributable to their powerful engines equipped with turbosuperchargers.

MORE POWER THAN BOULDER DAM

Besides the P-38, other planes equipped with the turbosupercharger included the P-47 Thunderbolt, PB4Y-1 Privateer, B-17 Flying Fortress, B-24 Liberator, B-29 Superfortress, and C-87 Liberator Express. The Flying Fortress required a turbosupercharger for each of its four engines, and the Superfortress two turbosuperchargers for each of its four engines. While the basic function of the eight "turbos" of the Superfortress was to feed enough oxygen into the four 2,200-horsepower engines to take the plane up above all antiaircraft fire, two of the "turbos" were used also to pressurize the cabin. This enabled the members of the crew to operate most of the time without oxygen masks, using them only during bombing runs or under conditions where there was serious danger of enemy missiles penetrating the cabin and causing loss of air pressure.

Up to the end of the war General Electric built 162,380 turbosuperchargers of various types. The additional power these devices gave to the planes totaled 160,000,000 horsepower—more than a hundred times the power generated at Boulder Dam and more than three times the output of all the nation's steam power plants combined.

After the conclusion of hostilities the 381st Bombardment Group of the Eighth Air Force in England sent Doctor Moss as a souvenir a turbosupercharger that had a top-ranking op-

erational record of having functioned flawlessly for more
than a thousand hours on Flying Fortress raids against German industrial and military targets. It has since been placed
in the Aviation Section of the Franklin Institute in Philadelphia.

Commenting on this record, Gen. H. H. Arnold, Commanding General of the Army Air Forces, said to Doctor
Moss:

It is peculiarly fitting that you should be the recipient of a
turbosupercharger that has successfully withstood the rigors of
1,004 combat hours on 102 missions against the enemy. Certainly
it is a significant symbol of the strides we have made since you
conceived the idea of supercharging engines more than two dec-
ades ago. Cordial congratulations.

A NEW KIND OF POWER PLANT

Out of the company's turbosupercharger experience sprang
another development that has been characterized as the
greatest single advance in the history of aircraft propulsion.
Sitting at his desk one day early in the summer of 1941, Vice-
president R. C. Muir received a long distance telephone call
from Washington.

"Have you an engineer familiar with aviation problems
who can go to England to investigate a new and very secret
device?" he was asked.

The query came from Gen. H. H. Arnold, Commanding
General of the U.S. Army Air Forces. Nothing was said about
the nature of the device. Muir replied that one of the company's engineers with these qualifications was already in
England, and that he would cable him to do the job.

At London next day, this engineer was told where to go
and whom to see. At his destination he was shown a new
type of airplane powered by a jet engine—the invention of
Group Captain Frank Whittle of the Royal Air Force.

He was permitted to inspect the plane, but he was not allowed to make notes or sketches of it lest they fall into the hands of spies. He returned to New York by plane, arriving about a month after Mr. Muir's telephone conversation with Washington. He reported his return to the General Electric Company but explained that he was not permitted to reveal anything of what he had done or seen until he had discussed the whole matter with the Army Air Forces at Washington.

Returning from Washington, he told Mr. Muir what he had seen and what the government had in mind. A few days later, Muir and a group of General Electric engineers were called to the War Department for a conference. There they met with the Assistant Secretary of War, General Arnold, and several other officers.

After emphasizing the need for absolute secrecy, General Arnold went to the safe in his office and took out a sealed package, which had been brought over from England by a special Army plane a few days before. It contained the drawings of the British jet-propulsion power plant.

Because of General Electric's experience in making turbo-superchargers, General Arnold explained, the War Department had selected the company to undertake the development of jet engines in the United States. Mr. Muir was asked if the company would tackle the job. A quick reply was desired, and Muir agreed on the spot. He promised to have something ready within 6 months, and the group returned to Schenectady.

The Army considered it highly important that no one should learn that jet-propulsion work was being undertaken in the United States. A small crew of the company's design engineers was taken off supercharger work, warned of the need for secrecy, and assigned to the new job at the River Works, Lynn. A few days later three mysterious packages arrived by plane from England. They were brought to the plant in an unmarked truck which followed a roundabout route from the Boston airport. Even persons attached to the airport did not know the nature of the packages, nor did the truckmen who brought them to the plant have any idea what they contained. Once the truck was inside the plant gate the driver's helpers were dismissed so that they would not know to what part of the huge factory the packages were delivered. Finally they were set down in an old building formerly used for the manufacture of street-lighting equipment. Special guards were stationed night and day outside the door with orders to allow no one to enter without proper authority. The packages contained a jet engine from England.

In the same plane with the packages came Col. Don Keirn of the U.S. Army Air Forces and three English engineers who had worked on the jet plane in that country. The Britishers scattered to different small hotels in the vicinity of Boston. From time to time they moved their residences so that their presence would not arouse curiosity.

Before long the original three engineers were joined by Group Captain Whittle, the English designer of the new type power plant, who remained in the United States for more than 3 months, though scarcely anyone knew it. On his arrival he registered at the Hotel Statler in Boston under an assumed name. He ate his meals in his room and had a private telephone installed that did not go through the regular hotel switchboard. The staff of the hotel considered him a somewhat eccentric Englishman, but gave him no further attention.

Fearing that his identity might be discovered in spite of these precautions, Group Captain Whittle later left the hotel and went to live at the home of one of the company's engineers. Even here his true identity was not known except to his host, until long after the captain's return to England.

So, for 2½ years the secret was strictly kept. Until the War Department was willing to release the information not more than a hundred people in the entire country knew that the United States was interested in jet propulsion for aircraft and that General Electric was building the engine.

JET-PROPULSION ENGINES

Jet propulsion was a revolutionary departure from accepted practice in motive power for airplanes. The principle of jet propulsion, in one form or another, is familiar to everyone. It relies upon the physical law that to every action there is an equal and opposite reaction. This reaction produces the "kick" when a rifle is fired. It is the underlying principle of the rotary lawn sprinkler, the jets of water going in one direction and the reaction causing the frame with the nozzles to revolve in the opposite direction.

In ancient Greece, Hero demonstrated jet propulsion by means of a rotating ball operated by jets of steam. Sir Isaac Newton designed a jet-propelled carriage in 1680, but it was never actually built. Nearly a hundred years ago in England Charles Golightly was experimenting with a jet-propelled airplane.

While the principle of jet propulsion was known long ago, a successful jet engine could not be built until mechanics, chemistry, and metallurgy had reached an advanced state of development. For example, in the field of metallurgy alone, the necessary materials have been available only in recent years, the most important of them having been developed in connection with G.E.'s manufacture of turbosuperchargers.

An aircraft jet engine requires a constant, large supply of air to the combustion chamber where the fuel is burned. Basically the jet engine built by General Electric consisted of four parts. At the front was a rotating impeller, which sucked in the air and forced it backward at high pressure through a series of ducts. From the ducts the compressed air passed into a combustion chamber, into which fuel was being admitted at the same time, and ignited. The hot gases of combustion were directed at the buckets of a turbine wheel, causing it to revolve at high speed. The rotation of the turbine operated the impeller at the front of the engine. After passing through the turbine wheel the hot gases rushed at terrific velocity out of the rear vent.

This arrangement has many advantages for the propulsion of aircraft. There is no propeller—the only moving part of the engine is the shaft with the compressor and turbine wheel. There is virtually no noise in the cockpit, only a dull rumble, and virtually no vibration. Moreover, there are no visible flames coming out of the exhaust.

WORLD'S FASTEST FIGHTING PLANE

By March, 1942—within the 6-month period set by Vice-president Muir in his original talk with General Arnold—General Electric had built and tested the first American-made engine, called the "I-16." By October four additional units had been built and test flights completed.

Experiments were continued throughout 1943, and innumerable difficulties were overcome. In addition to solving their own problems, the company's engineers were able to suggest practical solutions to problems of a similar nature that had arisen in England.

For example, the English were having trouble with the turbine buckets. General Electric supplied them with buckets made by the dental-casting method that had been developed for the supercharger program. Complete specifications were furnished so that manufacture could be started in England. Trouble from air pulsations in the impeller was encountered in both countries. This was overcome by a design modification suggested by G-E engineers. A third change eliminating vibration in the impeller blades was based on experience the company had previously had in building turbosuperchargers.

The first propellerless, jet-propelled plane to fly in the

United States was the P-59 Airacomet in October, 1942. It and following models powered by jet engines were so successful that the Army Air Forces decided that jet engines were needed in volume. General Electric, therefore, started to convert to this work at its big plant at Syracuse, where the turbine program for destroyer escorts had just been completed. Before long the entire plant with its more than 600,-000 square feet of floor space was devoted to the making of jet engines.

Early in 1945, the War Department startled the world by announcing the world's swiftest fighter plane, the jet-propelled P-80 Shooting Star. It was said to be faster than any plane ever flown before by either the Axis or the Allies and to have a top speed in excess of 600 miles per hour.

Pilots found the Shooting Star an easy plane to handle. Its performance was highly praised by Col. Bruce K. Holloway, veteran pilot of the 14th Air Force, who made a series of test flights with the new jet-propelled aircraft. He said,

The P-80 is hot, and it's easy to fly. The P-80 is so smooth and quiet that you can talk in a normal voice with the engine going full blast. What impressed me most was the absolute lack of vibration.

As soon as the Shooting Star picks up a little speed you really begin to appreciate the power. With the constant thrust the jet gives, you still have good acceleration in the higher brackets. Once the P-80 is wide open, it seems to float through the air with the greatest of ease.

Another step forward was made in the "axial-flow" jet engine. In this the air is forced through a number of stages in the compressor and is then forced almost in direct line into the combustion chambers. This arrangement results in an engine of smaller diameter with less wind resistance.

Closely allied to the jet engine was the "propjet." This was a wartime development but was not announced until after the end of hostilities. In this the turbine spins not only an air compressor but also a conventional propeller to supplement the jet action. This method of driving a propeller by means of a gas turbine removes the ceiling on power that has long hampered airplane designers. Reciprocating engines can reach 3,500 horsepower only with prohibitive complexity, but a gas turbine of 10,000 horsepower is entirely feasible, a possibility offering wide opportunities for aircraft propulsion in the future.

8

Electricity in the Air

AMERICA'S SUPERIORITY IN THE AIR was nowhere more clearly demonstrated than in the B-29 Superfortress—the mightiest airplane used in World War II. It could fly a 3,000-mile mission with ease and deliver a tremendous load of bombs on its target. One high-ranking Japanese officer is reported to have said that the B-29's hastened the end of the war by at least 6 months.

The first Superfortress raid on Japan was in the early summer of 1944, three years from the time when development work started. Throughout this period a constantly increasing personnel had been working in strictest secrecy for the great day.

Target of the first raid was the steel mills at Yawata, the "Japanese Pittsburgh," which was said to produce one-fifth of Japan's steel output. The Japs were stunned by the new bomber. Striking from a base in China which had been painstakingly prepared by the work of nearly three-quarters of a million coolies, the B-29's fulfilled the worst fears the Japs had felt since Jimmy Doolittle's bombers had visited Tokyo 2 years earlier. Eyewitness reports from airmen returning from the raid told of sheets of flame shooting high into the air as the bombs hit their target. Some observers estimated that

Japan's war production had been set back at least 14 months.

Because it could go far beyond the range of fighter protection, the B-29 was provided with superlative armament. So powerful was this armament that the enemy hesitated to send up fighters to oppose it. Returning pilots reported that the B-29's accomplished about half their missions without encountering any enemy fighters at all. Because it could fly higher than any other bombing plane, the B-29 experienced little trouble from antiaircraft fire. In a war abounding in remarkable achievements, the design and construction of the American B-29 was among the greatest.

An outstanding difference between American war planes in general and those of other nations was their greater use of electrical equipment. Before World War II came to its end, electricity was performing functions on airplanes far beyond the wildest dreams of the early pilots. In this respect the B-29 Superfortress outclassed all other planes.

Except for its main engines, the B-29 could be properly described as an "all-electric" plane. Throughout the ship, from nose to tail, from wing tip to wing tip, electricity was employed to perform all sorts of control and operating tasks, many of which had formerly been done by mechanical or hydraulic means.

ELECTRICAL EQUIPMENT OF THE B-29

To operate its guns, controls, and auxiliary apparatus the Superfortress had 170 electric motors, 26 motor-generator sets, and 15,000 feet of electric wiring. More components made by General Electric—from vacuum tubes to fuel-pump motors—went into the B-29 than into any other war fabrication job undertaken by the company. Every one of the company's major plants made a contribution of some sort—a generator, a motor, a lamp, an instrument, a special kind of wire, a heater, a turbosupercharger, a radio receiver, or something else.

Storage batteries could not, of course, provide the electric power supply for an airplane like the B-29. So many of them would have been needed that their weight would have been utterly prohibitive. Generators had to be provided. Six units were used, gear-connected to the main engines. Each unit was of 9-kilowatt capacity, giving the plane a total generating capacity of 54 kilowatts—sufficient to provide all the power required to run ten modern, all-electric homes. These generators were made at the River Works, Lynn.

Essential to the power-supply system were the voltage regulators, which were made at Schenectady. As the engines that drove the generators operated at widely varying speeds, careful regulation of voltage was necessary to the proper operation of the plane's electric system.

Once the power was generated, it had to be distributed to the points where it was needed. For this purpose the company designed a special line of aircraft wire that was flame-proof, small in diameter, light in weight, flexible at extreme temperatures, and resistant to oil, moisture, and solvents.

Among the tasks performed electrically were (1) raising and lowering landing wheels, (2) opening and closing landing-wheel doors, (3) operating brakes on landing wheels, (4) raising and lowering landing flaps, (5) opening and closing ventilators, (6) opening and closing bomb-bay doors, (7) rotating gun turrets, (8) raising and lowering the elevation of the guns, and (9) changing the pitch of the propellers.

MOTORS AND INSTRUMENTS

Electricity was a prominent factor in the operations of many other airplanes besides the B-29. For this purpose a special line of fractional-horsepower motors was provided in a wide variety of sizes. One type for delicate control devices was only 1⅝ inches in diameter and weighed but a few ounces. It was so small that it rested snugly in the palm of the hand. For other purposes, such as the operation of landing gear, pumps, and similar heavy apparatus, much larger motors were required. Rating on these motors ran as high as 10 or 15 horsepower. Practically all the airplane motors were made at the Fort Wayne Works.

Instruments were the nerve centers of all aircraft. These were of two types—engine and flight. The first told the pilot what he needed to know about his engine and its operation—speed or rotation, gasoline level, oil pressure, temperature, and the like. The second type provided information concerning the flight of the plane—speed, direction, altitude, and so on.

Most of these instruments were electric, and millions of them were built at the West Lynn Works. This had not been a large-scale activity there before the war, though aeronautical compasses had been made during World War I and a skeleton crew had continued in the ensuing years to work on basic developments in aircraft instruments. With the outbreak of World War II, the knowledge and experience gained in making a wide variety of electric measuring devices was immediately put to work to design new and better instruments for airplanes.

The d-c selsyn system was developed by engineers at West Lynn. This was a simple arrangement whereby movements that were detected by a transmitter were sent electrically to an indicator on the instrument panel in the cockpit. It was first used for landing gear and flap-position indicators. The next instruments to which the selsyn system was applied were gasoline gauges. Later it was applied to temperature- and pressure-indicating equipment.

Combat experience in Africa and Alaska indicated a need for better gyroscopic instruments. Dust and extremes of high and low temperature put air-driven gyros out of order. Electric drive proved to be the solution. Four types were made at West Lynn: a horizon indicator, a direction indicator, a horizontal control, and a directional control.

Manufacture of glass jewels for instrument bearings was an important contribution by West Lynn. The war cut off the normal supply of sapphire jewels, which had been coming mostly from Switzerland, and the situation of the instrument makers in the United States had become desperate by the early part of 1942. But G-E engineers, foreseeing the need for jewels, had accelerated the development of a V-shaped jewel of special hard glass and a method of making it. At the peak of production these artificial jewels were being turned out at a rate of 360,000 a week. The company itself used about 16 per cent of the output, the remainder going to other manufacturers of electric instruments.

Electricity played a part even in the operation of the magnetic compass on airplanes. As everyone knows, a pocket compass must be held at some distance away from iron or steel objects to give the correct direction. Similarly, an airplane must have its compass located in some place where iron or steel will not affect it, as in a wing tip, or in the tail —but the pilot must still be able to read it in the cockpit. To meet this situation General Electric developed a remote-indicating compass wherein the exact reading of the actual compass was electrically reproduced on a dial in front of the pilot.

AUTOMATIC PILOT

Finally, after having developed a wide variety of instruments to aid the pilot in the control of his plane, General Electric developed an automatic pilot, which almost eliminated the need for human control in flight. This device combined an electrically driven gyroscope with controls that actuated rudders, ailerons, and elevators, maintaining a plane on a given course without attention from the pilot.

It is a characteristic of the gyroscope that it maintains a fixed axis of rotation regardless of gravity, magnetism, or the earth's rotation. It resists any attempt to change the direction of its axis while spinning. When a ship or an airplane deviates from its correct course, a gyroscope mounted horizontally still points in a fixed direction, permitting automatic indication of how far the craft is off its course. Another gyroscope mounted vertically in a plane indicates deviation from a predetermined angle of climb, descent, or horizontal course.

With the automatic pilot it was possible to set the controls for the course that the pilot wished to follow and leave the rest to the automatic mechanism. Any pitch, roll, or yaw—that is, any lengthwise or crosswise tilt or turn—caused the gyroscope to send a tiny electrical impulse to an amplifier, where it was converted into a greater volume of electrical energy and sent on to a "servo" power unit. This proceeded to alter the position of the elevators, ailerons, or rudder to bring the plane back to its correct course.

The primary function of the automatic pilot was to provide relief for the human pilot by taking over the controls and maintaining the course he set. Actually it did more than provide relief; it held the plane steadier than human hands could do. On a long straight-line flight the automatic mechanism did not permit the plane to deviate more than one-half of one degree from its set course, and it was quicker than a live pilot in making corrections for deviations.

REMOTE TURRET CONTROL

Most spectacular of the uses of electricity on aircraft was remote turret control. The earliest method of fire control on aircraft, still used on single-place fighters, was to use fixed guns and point the plane at the target. Next came the revolving gun turret. At first this was manually operated, but that was impracticable at high speeds because of the heavy wind loads. The need for power to revolve the turrets swiftly was partly met by employing hydraulic operation for gun turrets for interceptor fighters and bombers.

Then General Electric designed and built an electrically operated turret. This was in large measure the outgrowth of work done by the company's Aeronautics and Marine Engineering Division in solving gunfire-control problems for the Navy in World War I. With the new system, two 50-caliber machine guns were controlled by a gunner seated in the turret.

This design, greatly superior in speed, safety, and flexibility to manually and hydraulically operated turrets, was used in such Navy planes as the Avenger and Ventura and in the Army's B-24, B-25, and B-26 bombers. Once a dependable, power-driven method was available to swing and point heavy guns, long-range bombers could undertake missions beyond the range of fighter escorts.

At the same time that work was under way on these locally controlled electric turrets, the company's engineers set out to see what could be done to control a machine-gun turret in a large bomber from a remote point within the cabin. So promising were the results of these experiments that, shortly before Pearl Harbor, the Army Air Forces asked the company to design a remote-control system for its huge new B-29 Superfortress, then in the early stages of development.

Within a period of a few months, the seventy engineers assigned to the project had completed the designing and testing work. A shop for the assembly of the turrets was set up at the Erie Works. Many of the parts were manufactured at Erie, but other of the company's plants also contributed items of types in which they specialized.

For example, the air compressors for gun chargers were made at the Bloomfield Works. Guns firing 500 or more rounds per minute sometimes encountered "misfires," which caused jamming because the mechanical ejecting device was designed to handle only used shells. A device operated by electricity alone could not perform this function effectively, since the force required to eject a jammed shell was so great that bulky and weighty equipment would have been necessary. The problem before the designers of these compressors was primarily one of meeting requirements for low weight. This was done by the use of magnesium alloys. Because of its unusually high compression ratio (350:1, as compared with the 15:1 ratio of the average compressor), the manufacture of this equipment was a precision process with extremely close tolerances of physical measurement and compressor capacity. The compressors supplied high-pressure air capable of ejecting any "dud" or any shell jammed in the gun's breech, and helped ensure maximum efficiency of the guns during combat.

The first remote-control turret was delivered in August, 1942, and a production schedule was established of 600 turrets per month. Before long, however, the Army Air Forces requested an expansion of facilities to permit the manufacture of 2,400 turrets per month. At the height of the war production this project was demanding the combined talents and efforts of some 20,000 General Electric workers and thousands more at the plants of dozens of subcontractors.

THE "BATTLE OF KANSAS"

Manufacture of the equipment for the remote-control system was only part of the problem. After the Superfortresses began to roll off the assembly line they had to be fitted with the myriad pieces of apparatus that would make them the most powerful, longest range bombers in the world.

On a snow-swept airfield in Kansas a great throng of technicians gathered from General Electric and other companies that had made gear for the B-29. It was their job to see that the equipment was properly installed and that any necessary, last minute modifications were made. The pressure was terrific. Working facilities were inadequate. Elbow room was nil. Telephone wires between the airfield and other parts of the country vibrated with rush orders. Flashlights flickered at night all over the huge airfield as the men worked.

A deadline had been set for the completion of the job. Every problem had to be overcome at the highest possible speed. For example, a last minute change had to be made in the gunfire interrupter mechanism—a device to limit the possible movement of the guns so that they could not fire through the wings or tail of their own plane. A cam of special dimensions was needed. None was available. A telephone call to Schenectady disclosed that the tools required to make it were there, but the right men for the job were at Bloomfield. So the tools were shipped to New Jersey, the cams were machined there, and were then flown to Kansas. The "Battle of Kansas," the men called it, and everyone sighed with relief as, one after another, the completed planes took to the air.

RCT IN COMBAT

The remote-control turret system for the B-29 consisted of five gun turrets, electrically connected with five gun sights through five computers. The turrets were above and below the fuselage at the front end, above and below the fuselage about two-thirds of the way toward the back, and at the very tail of the plane.

The guns were sighted from one or more stations in the nose, tail, and along the sides of the fuselage. Then the mechanical computers worked out corrections for speed, wind drift, parallex, and other factors, and the control mechanisms made the necessary adjustments in the aiming of the guns. As the process of computing was virtually instantaneous, the gunner could sight on his target and fire immediately with perfect assurance that the electrical system was directing the gun so that the projectile and the enemy plane at which he was firing would arrive simultaneously at the same point.

With this remote turret control it became possible for the first time for the entire crew of a big bomber to be placed in a heated and pressurized cabin, well protected by armor. Except in emergency, they could move unhampered by heated flying suits or oxygen masks. Since the gunners no longer needed to man their turrets, extra space was available for ammunition automatically fed to the guns.

Reports received from bombardment units of the Army Air Forces spoke of this system of remote turret control as being "vastly superior to any other method employed in this war." Its effectiveness was indicated by the fact that in one theater of operations, an average of 494 attacks by enemy aircraft was required to shoot down a single B-29.

DESIGN OF THE B-36

Remarkable as was the B-29, it was surpassed in size by the later B-36. Conceived at a time when nobody knew when, if ever, the United States would be able to secure air bases reasonably close to the Japanese home islands, the B-36 was designed to fly missions from bases in the Hawaiian Islands or the U.S. mainland direct to Japan. It was nearly twice the size of the B-29, had six engines, and a possible flying range of 10,000 miles. To operate its varied electric equipment, 120 kilowatts of generating capacity were required as compared with only 54 kilowatts on the Superfortress.

This large increase in the use of electric power necessitated far-reaching changes in the whole electrical system of the plane. To distribute 120 kilowatts of power at the low voltage previously used would have required conductors of such large size that the weight of conductor would have been absolutely prohibitive. It was decided, therefore, to generate and distribute at 400 cycles 120 volts alternating current instead of 30 volts direct current, and the Army came to General Electric for help in planning the new equipment. Extended investigations in which the General Engineering

Laboratory took an active part led to the design of an entirely new electric system that performed in a highly satisfactory manner in early tests. Use of alternating current was particularly advantageous for radar and other electronic equipment. No B-36's were completed in time to participate in actual conflict, but the developments in connection with this giant plane promised to have wide future application.

9

Aids for Fighters

Hᴀʀᴅsʜɪᴘ ʜᴀs ᴀʟᴡᴀʏs ʙᴇᴇɴ supposed to be a necessary part of a soldier's life, but the United States Army in World War II believed that discomfort lowered the soldier's efficiency and it took every practicable step to eliminate physical hardship. Electric devices of various sorts were instrumental in this endeavor.

Ways to combat the crippling cold of flying in the substratosphere where temperatures got down as low as 70 degrees below zero Fahrenheit had been receiving careful study by the Army Air Forces for some time before the beginning of the war. Household electric blankets were then in production at Bridgeport.

This blanket consisted essentially of heating wires placed in staggered channels woven in two layers of the material, with a control mechanism to regulate the flow of electric current. In the summer of 1940 the War Department asked General Electric to develop a lightweight, electrically heated flying suit, based on the principle of the electric blanket, so that the Army's fliers could operate their planes at high altitudes free of the encumbrance of heavy clothing. Along with the suit itself, the outfit was to include gloves and boots.

ELECTRICALLY HEATED FLYING SUITS

Working at top speed, the company developed and delivered a sample within 12 days. This sample was a standard AAF summer flying suit, in which had been placed heating wires of suitable weight, flexibility, and resistance in parallel lines. Fine leather gloves, of material commonly used in women's dress gloves, were wired on the back and at the wrists, giving warmth and yet permitting the sense of touch required for handling delicate flying equipment. Boots were heated by means of inserts shaped like a clover leaf in which wires were cemented between the two layers of material. The complete electrical assembly consisted of four circuits, one for gloves, one for boot inserts, and two for the suit, all connected to a switch box which was in turn connected through a control box to the power source. This arrangement permitted independent regulation of heat in gloves, boots, or suit.

The Army was well pleased with the initial design and promptly placed an order for fifteen suits with several suggested improvements. Delivery was requested within 6 weeks, as some of the suits were to be tested on a cold weather experimental flight of bombers in Alaska.

These first suits were designed and produced with little background knowledge. There were no precedents to follow. No one knew where heat was required in a flying suit in order to make it comfortable under all conditions. Medical men were consulted. Writings of Arctic explorers were studied. Advice was secured from medical laboratories and from the company's Research Laboratory at Schenectady. The manager of the Pioneer Products Division at Bridgeport obtained permission to conduct tests in the freezing room of a local ice cream plant, in a vegetable refrigerator, and in a cold-storage room for holding frozen fish. Many experiments were conducted in these places with the effects of cold on the body. Later the company built its own cold room at the Bridgeport Works.

Manufacturing, however, could not wait for these tests to be completed. Suits of some sort had to be made in a hurry, and early designs were based on the best guesses available. Heavy woolen union suits, chosen for their elasticity and thermal insulating qualities, were the foundation of the first fifteen test suits. They were to be worn under an ordinary Army uniform and a summer flying suit in order to secure the maximum heat utilization. Wires were to be sewed in parallel waves to secure an accordion effect which could stretch with the wool and conform to bodily movements with the least amount of stress on the wires. The switch box was eliminated, and the connection between the suit and the control box was improved to provide quick disconnection in case the wearer had to bail out of his plane. The finished suits were then tested in cold rooms at temperatures of 35 degrees, zero, and 50 degrees below zero, with a final testing at 63 degrees below zero at Fort Monmouth.

Then came the flight tests in Alaska. They showed the need for further improvements, and a revised design was developed in February, 1941. This had an outer shell of two-ply, blue, all-wool material, cut on the bias for elasticity, with the wires sewed on the inside. Cotton flannel was used for lining because it was comfortable against the body. The clover-leaf shoe insert was supplanted by a wired cloth shoe of olive drab overcoating material with molded rubber soles. This was worn inside a standard light aviation boot. Cape-skin gloves with short gauntlets were provided. Stranded copper wire was used throughout, with gloves and shoes in series to produce sufficient resistance.

This design was accepted by the Army Air Forces in April, 1941, and in July the company received an order for 12,000 outfits. In November an additional contract was received for 40,000 suits.

Because this suit was intended for wear under a flying suit, and without a uniform, it was considered to be dangerous for fliers who might be forced down over enemy territory. They ran the risk of being shot as spies. Moreover, it was not warm enough in case of electrical failure, and therefore another model was designed.

The new design was a carefully tailored, dark khaki gabardine jumper-type overall and jacket, which simulated a regular uniform. This type suit proved to be too good-looking to be practical. Pilots wore it everywhere—at parties, for excursions into town, for playing football, and on many other occasions instead of saving it for use in the air. For this reason a third model was developed late in 1943 and put into production early in 1944. It was a lightweight khaki jumper-type overall and jacket worn between a uniform and a flying suit.

After the first stage of experimentation had passed, demands for the electrically heated flying suits multiplied so rapidly that additional production facilities were opened at Lowell, Mass., and New Milford, Conn. Staffed largely by women, these facilities could turn out 8,000 suit assemblies per week. Altogether a total of more than 400,000 suits were made by the company.

THE COPPER MAN

Testing of the suits was a never-ending performance. When the company first undertook to make electrically heated clothing for fliers, data were obtained by cut-and-try methods, which involved human guinea pigs sitting for long hours in refrigerated test chambers. Then it was decided to develop a mechanical device that would simulate the human body. So General Electric's "copper man" was born. His proportions were those of the average Air Force flier—5 feet 10½ inches tall—and his copper skin was 1/16 inch thick.

A complicated system of electric wires connected with separate areas of the copper head, torso, hands, and feet to reproduce the temperature variations that occur in different parts of the human body. Altogether the body was divided into fifteen areas, the amount of electrical energy supplied to each area being subject to individual control. The temperature of the "man" could be made to vary from subnormal to above normal. A dummy head was provided to breathe air having a controllable content of moisture. Thus, it was possible to determine what clothing was adequate under any desired conditions without subjecting human beings to suffering or danger.

Experiments in refrigerated rooms and altitude chambers were supplemented by a series of outdoor tests. No test was too rough, no research too painstaking, no study too complicated to be undertaken. A group of the company's engineers and technicians put the suit through a series of rigorous try-outs on Mount Washington, N.H. Field trials included skiing, hiking, working, trail blazing, and camping out for a 2-day period. In every instance the clothing proved to be sturdy and efficient.

HEATED GOGGLES FOR FLYING

From its success with the electrically heated flying suit, the Pioneer Products Division went on to a wide variety of other electrically heated aids. While testing flying suits in the summer of 1941 at the Fort Monmouth Signal Corps Laboratories, one of the company's engineers found that at the test temperature of 65 degrees below zero, he suffered considerable pain in back of the eyes. Icicles formed around his eyes and the lashes froze together. He realized that some protection was needed to prevent this condition and he tried ordinary goggles. The lenses frosted over in a few minutes, however, and the goggles became useless. At high altitudes such fogging would have necessitated the removal of the goggles at the risk of frostbitten eyeballs.

This fogging and frosting came from condensation on the lenses of moisture given off by the eyes and skin. Ventilation of the goggles would have helped, but the ventilation necessary to prevent frosting high aloft was extremely uncomfortable and dangerous at the prevalent low temperatures. Pioneer Products Division then began the design and development of goggle heaters without waiting for a request from the Army.

One of the early complications was to find a quick and economical way of modifying the goggle already in use. Six heating methods were tried out on actual models. These included heating wires near the lenses, in contact with the lenses, embedded in the lenses, and placed between double lenses, as well as various methods of radiation and conduction of heat from the rims. Experiments indicated the best method to be that of employing a wire grid in contact with the lens. This could be done easily with clip-on units as adaptors for the unheated goggles currently in use. The Army Air Forces approved this model and ordered 500 of them for trial.

A little later the Army Air Forces looked favorably on plastics lenses in a molded rubber frame. This presented an opportunity to design a plastics lens without the restriction of adapting heating arrangements to existing designs. Wire between plastics sheets seemed the most satisfactory answer, but could it be sealed in place permanently to protect it from moisture and handling? On a suggestion from the plastics industry two sheets of plastics were placed on either side of a wired sheet, which had been wound in accordance with a prearranged pattern. The whole assembly was then laminated under heat and pressure into a single, moistureproof, homogeneous plastics sheet.

Liking the samples, the AAF placed a small order. When

Bombs being placed in bomb bay of an AAF Flying Fortress at a flying field in England.

Turbosupercharged Thunderbolts—outstanding high-altitude fighters.

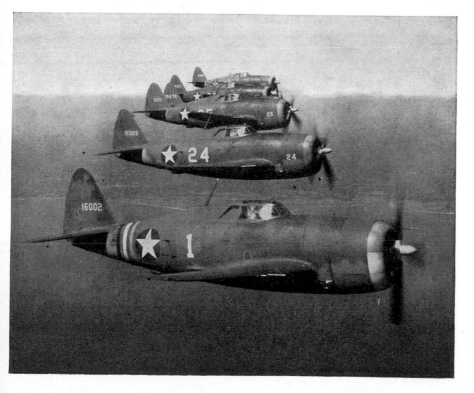

Superfortress dropping its deadly "eggs" on a Jap steel plant. These planes—largest used in World War II, had two turbosuperchargers for each engine.

Production line at one of G.E.'s turbosupercharger plants.

Test chamber with 4-inch steel walls, where turbosuperchargers were rotated at 25,000 revolutions per minute to discover possible defects.

Turbine wheel, impeller and shaft for jet engine.

Diffuser for distributing air to combustion chambers of jet engine.

Assembling the 14 chambers in which the combustion takes place.

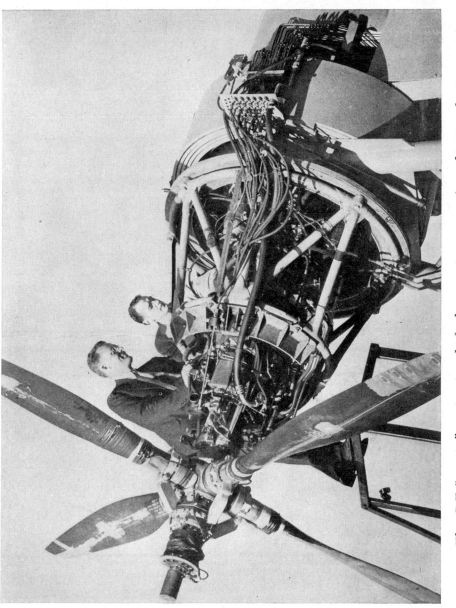

The G-E "propjet" engine in which the escaping gases of combustion drive a propeller by means of a gas turbine and boost with jet action.

The P-59, Airacomet, the first American jet propelled
plane, powered by twin G-E engines.

Speed record holder of World War II, the jet-propelled
P-80 Shooting Star. The speedometer had a maximum
reading of 800 miles an hour.

One of many types of special, fractional horsepower
motors produced by G.E. for use on aircraft.

A few of the millions of aircraft instruments which the
company made during the war. Those shown here are
illuminated by an ultraviolet lighting system.

Aircraft searchlight mounted under starboard wing of a PB4Y.

Lethal load—placing bombs aboard a Flying Fortress.

Two-gun aircraft turret designed for power operation by remote control.

Rear sighting position for remote control of turrets.

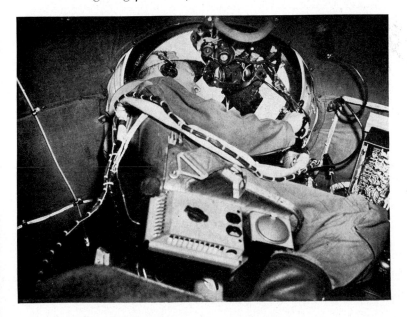

Final assembly for remote control turrets at the Erie Works.

American flyers wearing electrically heated flying suits enter plane before take-off of bombing flight to Continent.

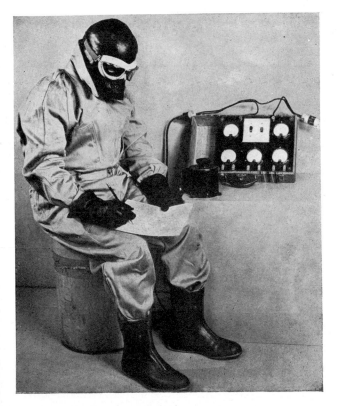

Electrically heated flying suits being tested at 63 degrees below zero.

Testing the electrically heated flying suits—a group of G-E engineers give them a vigorous tryout on Mt. Washington.

Copper-man—a mechanical device to test clothing without subjecting humans to long hours of discomfort.

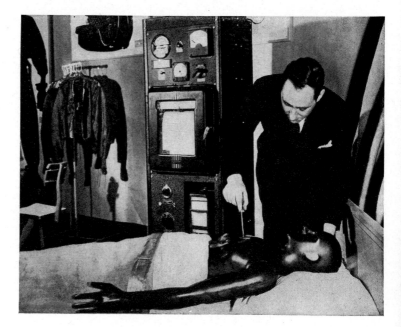

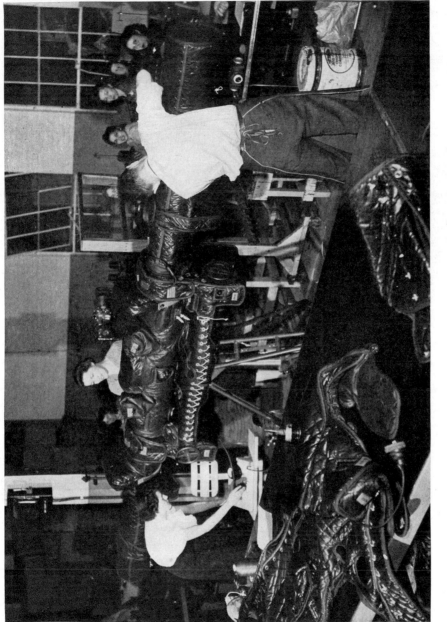

Making electrically heated covers at the Bridgeport Works.

Electrically heated oxygen mask—one of numerous developments growing out of the electrically heated flying suits.

Problems resulting from low temperatures at high altitudes extended to instruments and apparatus—a variety of electrically heated covers is shown here.

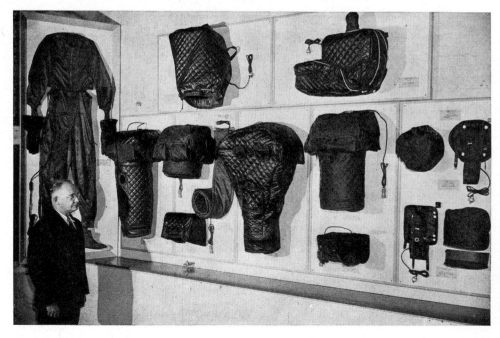

production started, however, it was found that dust and fingerprints were being trapped in the lenses. On the spot a crude air-conditioning system was built to overcome this contamination. Although a makeshift arrangement, it cleared away that difficulty. So successful were these goggles that the AAF placed an order for 15,000 pairs to be shipped at the earliest possible moment and for 15,000 pairs to be shipped each week thereafter.

In preparing for mass production, no time was allowed for the customary planning and installation of the air conditioning needed, nor for the usual production-planning operations. The whole development had to be done on the job—and fast.

In 12 short days and nights a storage floor was converted into a modern air-conditioned room with good illumination and the necessary production equipment. Arrangements were made for accurate lamination, finishing, testing, and inspection of the goggles. Special airtight boxes were developed for shipping the lenses so that lamination could be done at Lynn, Mass., assembly at Bridgeport, Conn., and finishing and inspection at New Milford, Conn.

On the thirteenth day operators dressed in lintless white smocks and rayon gloves started to work. Seated on high chairs with special back rests, their fingers flew as they threaded oxidized nickel wire, as fine as human hair, over the raised nibs on a plastics sheet. This work was done on framed glass panels, inclined like a drawing board and illuminated from the rear. Frequent rest periods were given the operators to eliminate eyestrain. A special shadowgraph was made and used as an enlarger for the use of the inspectors.

Just as success seemed assured, air pockets in the laminated sheets of plastics were found to be causing blisters in the finished lenses. Again feverish experiments were undertaken. Finally this, too, was corrected by punching holes in the outer plastics sheet to allow the air to escape. After this final crisis, production went rolling along to everyone's satisfaction. By the end of the war more than 220,000 pairs of these electrically heated goggles had been produced and delivered to the Army Air Forces.

OTHER ELECTRICALLY HEATED DEVICES

The problems resulting from low temperatures at high altitudes were not confined to clothing and goggles. It was found that the fliers' oxygen masks often choked up with ice as the moisture from the airmen's breath froze. So electric heaters were developed for various different types of oxygen masks. It was also discovered that substratosphere cold affected the accuracy of the bombsight, and an electrically heated cover was devised for it. The Bridgeport Works produced a total of some 70,000 covers. Similarly, the company designed an electrically heated cover for the automatic pilot and an electric blanket for wounded airmen.

Another job involved the design of a heated cover for the cameras used in high-altitude flying. It had been found that subzero temperatures made intricate camera mechanisms inoperative. Development had been in progress for some time when a request came from the War Department at 4:30 P.M. on a Friday for delivery of a sample design the following Monday morning. A group of engineers was hastily assembled. At 4:45 P.M. they gathered around a wooden model of the camera. The irregular shape presented difficulties. They began to make cloth patterns to determine how the lining and outer shell material could most advantageously be cut. After many experiments a satisfactory pattern was finally selected, and they knocked off work just before midnight.

Next morning a quantity of special heating wire was run off the insulating machine. After lunch a girl started sewing wire into the blanket. This work was completed by four o'clock Saturday afternoon. Then the cover was placed on a metal dummy of the camera and put into a refrigerator for thermal tests at 60 degrees below zero Fahrenheit.

These tests disclosed shortcomings in the original design. At eight o'clock on Sunday morning work was commenced on an improved model that was completed by late afternoon of the same day. Early Monday morning the improved model was turned over to an Army officer who immediately boarded a plane and flew it to Wright Field. Thus, a new and valuable war product was designed and turned out in the short space of a single week end.

EMERGENCY SIGNALING MIRROR

Among the many new accessories developed during the war to aid the members of the American armed forces were two simple devices that saved many lives at sea. When a flier is compelled to come down in the ocean, or a sailor is cast adrift in an open boat, his chance of survival depends to a large extent upon his ability to make his plight and position known to possible rescuers. To accomplish this during hours of darkness, the Lamp Department made a tiny electric light for life jackets. It was operated by a small dry battery. Lamp and battery were attached to the life jacket behind the right shoulder. Its bright light could be seen for a long distance at night and was instrumental in the rescue of many a man whose plight might never have been known without it.

For use in daylight hours an emergency signaling mirror was developed by the Lamp Department, cooperating with the U.S. Bureau of Standards. A brilliant flash of sunlight from a shiny surface is one of the surest ways of attracting attention. To be an effective safety device, however, a signaling mirror must stay bright and perfectly flat under all conditions, and it must be provided with some means whereby it can be aimed accurately at a ship on the distant horizon or a plane miles away in the sky.

The emergency signaling mirror was a pocket-size device, utilizing the process employed in making the reflectors in the company's Sealed Beam Headlamp. It was of tempered glass covered with a film of vaporized aluminum. The glass was highly resistant to fragmentation. In the unlikely event of breakage it disintegrated into small blunt crystals instead of dangerous sharp splinters. It had a central, cross-shaped aperture surrounded by a circle of exposed rear surface of the mirror film that permitted it to be aimed with great accuracy at a target miles away.

Hundreds of thousands of these "solar searchlights" placed on lifeboats and rafts on American vessels and aircraft were the means of saving many lives. Most dramatic, perhaps, was the rescue of a Navy flier who was compelled to make a forced landing in Tokyo's outer bay. After his plane had gone down his comrades in other planes started a search for him. Fortunately, he had an emergency signaling mirror with him and the sun was shining. He began to flash his location to his comrades high above the water and quickly attracted their attention. Like a sea gull diving for a fish one of them swooped down from the sky and snatched him out of danger —from under the very noses of the enemy.

10

Weapons for the Army

ON A MAY MORNING IN 1942, a couple of G-E engineers arrived at the Bridgeport Works with preliminary sketches and models of a proposed new weapon, the "Launcher, Rocket, AT, M-1," together with a letter purchase order for the company to "design, develop, and produce" 5,000 of them within 30 days. This was a job that would ordinarily have required 6 months, but the Army was in a hurry. The assignment was so important that it took precedence over all other ordnance jobs in the entire country.

DEVELOPMENT OF THE BAZOOKA

In the early days of the war the Germans went in for tanks in a big way. They seemed virtually irresistible. American officers were worried because the infantry had nothing with which to combat them effectively. Finally a rocket-type weapon was devised that military men believed would do the job. The principle of an armor-piercing projectile that did not need high striking velocity was 50 years old, but the method of launching the projectile was new. That was what the Army was asking the company to develop and put into production in 30 days. Representatives of the company had known that this was under consideration, but the actual production demand came suddenly.

After looking over the drawings, Bridgeport agreed to undertake the job. Within 24 hours the first design was drawn up. Four days later a couple of models were delivered to the Army for testing, and by the end of May the number had grown to 20. For more than 2 weeks the new weapon was tested and retested.

Essentially, the rocket launcher was a tube of approximately 2½-inch diameter, 5 feet long, with open ends, equipped with sights and an electric firing mechanism. A rocket was inserted through one end, the tube was placed in firing position over the right shoulder of the soldier, and it was aimed at the target. Then the trigger was pulled and the rocket was on its way. Because the rocket was propelled by the jet action of gases released continuously from within itself and the launcher tube had open ends, it did not kick back like a rifle where the propelling force is obtained by an explosion in an enclosed space.

The new weapon weighed only about 18 pounds. It was so light that it could easily be handled by two men—one in an emergency—yet it fired a projectile that could knock out a tank. Soldiers dubbed it the "bazooka" because they saw in it some remote resemblance to the weird musical instrument made famous by Bob Burns, the Arkansas comedian.

When the tests had been completed and the samples approved, there remained just 8 days in which to manufacture the thousands of bazookas that the Army wanted to have within 30 days from the time development started. Materials were rushed to the plant. Truck drivers worked in relays around the clock to bring the steel from Pittsburgh. One shipment was made by airplane.

While speeding to the factory with a car full of gunstocks, an Army Ordnance officer was stopped by state police for speeding. When he told them what the material was for, the police provided an escort to help rush the shipment to the production line. As the bazookas came off the line they were hustled into waiting Army trucks, and were on their way to a port of embarkation before the stain on the gunstocks was really dry. The last of the 5,000 bazookas of this big job came off the line on the eighth day with 89 minutes to spare before the expiration of the Army's time limit.

THE BAZOOKA IN NORTH AFRICA

Development of the bazooka took the Germans completely by surprise. Up to that time their tanks had enjoyed remarkable success. But the bazooka stopped them cold. They never really recovered the initiative after the first stunning blows struck by this weapon, which was frequently characterized as the most important ordnance development of the war.

North Africa was the scene of the bazooka's initial success. The first of these weapons were issued to troops aboard ships of the invasion armada. Although the troops had no opportunity for actual practice with them, they familiarized themselves thoroughly with their general construction and operation. When, in the dark hours before dawn on the morning of Nov. 8, 1942, the assault boats headed for the shore at Algiers, Oran, and Casablanca, the bazookas went with them.

Where a small but strong coastal fort was giving considerable trouble to the American invaders, one lone soldier detached himself from his landing party, waded ashore by himself, and with one shot from his bazooka, secured the surrender of the fort. On another occasion, after the landing had been completed, a shot from a bazooka struck a tree near a group of six enemy tanks. The commander of the tanks was so startled that he surrendered the whole group of them, believing that he was being shelled by 155-millimeter artillery.

"The bazooka is so simple and yet so powerful," said Maj.

Gen. L. H. Campbell, Jr., Chief of Army Ordnance, "that a foot soldier using it can stand his ground with the certain knowledge that he is the master of any tank which may attack him."

FOLDING AND FLYING BAZOOKAS

The first type of bazooka had a single-piece steel barrel with a permanent rear sight, similar to that of an ordinary rifle. Next came a streamlined, take-apart model, commonly known as the "folding bazooka." This was designed for use by paratroopers and infantrymen fighting in jungles and thick underbrush. It had the important advantages of easier handling and less likelihood of snagging the weapon on vines and thus impeding the progress of the attack. This model had no fixed sights on the barrel, but only a single-element bar sight which folded against the side of the barrel when not in use.

The success of the bazooka in ground operations led the Army to consider the possibilities of an air-borne rocket launcher. General Electric was asked to develop a type that would be mounted in clusters of three on the under side of the wings of a number of different types of fighter planes. The barrels were of 4½ inch diameter and were 10 feet long. At first these launchers were made from steel tubes, but the 200-pound weight of this cluster was more than could be tolerated on planes on military missions.

To meet this situation the Plastics Division at Pittsfield developed a special fire-resistant plastic. A good-grade, high-strength paper, impregnated with resin, was used. This reduced the weight to about 80 pounds per cluster or 160 pounds per plane. Thousands of bazookas were also made of magnesium alloy. All six barrels of the two clusters could be fired simultaneously, or each barrel could be fired individually.

Light in weight, and without recoil or kick, the air-borne

rocket launcher had decided advantages over a gun of the same size. Planes carrying these bazooka clusters were often called "flying artillery." They came in low to blast ammunition dumps, airfields, barracks, and gun emplacements as well as ships, barges, and small boats. In France they were credited with contributing to the destruction of the German Seventh Army in its retreat from the Falaise pocket by constantly harassing the enemy's motorized columns.

Another development was the rocket launcher for tanks. These weapons were carried in a rack mounted above the turret. Each tank had a total of sixty launchers. They could be fired singly, in groups of five, or in one tremendous salvo, with each rocket leaving its tube a half second after the previous one. When all rockets had been fired the rack was automatically jettisoned and the tank went into action with its regular 75-millimeter gun. The rack was later salvaged and used for a repeat performance.

A featherweight bazooka for the infantry was a still later development. This had an aluminum barrel and weighed only a little over 10 pounds. It had improved sights and firing mechanism.

Late in 1944, the thousands of employees of the Bridgeport Works assembled in a huge mass meeting to greet Undersecretary of War Robert P. Patterson, who had come there for the purpose of receiving officially the 300,000th bazooka the company had produced. After outlining some of the performances of the bazooka in action, Mr. Patterson remarked feelingly that "The Ordnance Department knew what it was doing when it gave the production job to the men and women of this plant. It knew that you would not fail them, and you did not fail them."

MAKING PACK HOWITZERS

Another weapon built for the Army was the 75-millimeter pack howitzer. Its manufacture at the Erie Works was the first instance during World War II of guns as large as this being made outside of government arsenals. This wouldn't have happened except for an unusual chain of circumstances.

Back in the latter part of 1938 and early in 1939, when general industrial activity was at a low level, the management of the Erie Works was concerned over the number of machines standing idle in the plant. At this time the War Department was following a policy of placing small educational orders for war material with private manufacturers so that they would be better prepared to assist the government in time of emergency. The works management thought that this might offer a means of putting some of the idle machines back into production, and approval was obtained from the company's general sales committee to enter into negotiations with the War Department.

Consultation between plant officials and Army Ordnance indicated that the making of most of the equipment for which contracts were then being let required boring machines of larger capacity than any that were available at Erie. It developed, however, that the War Department was intending in the near future to invite bids on the manufacture of 75-millimeter pack howitzers, the barrel of which was approximately 50 inches long and could be bored on the machine ordinarily used for making electric railway motors, though special machines would have to be obtained for rifling.

The 75-millimeter pack howitzer was an old weapon, originally designed for mule transport. Though mechanization had reduced the Army's use of mule transport, the pack howitzer remained an extremely useful weapon because of its easy portability. It had the heaviest striking power for its weight of any gun the Army possessed. It fired a comparatively heavy shell, but the entire assembly weighed only about 1,200 pounds. The howitzer could be transported by motor truck or airplane or boat without being disassembled.

It could be carried in disassembled packs and dropped by parachute. Having been taken apart, it could be put together again and made ready to fire in 8 minutes.

The need for quick assembly greatly complicated the manufacture of the howitzer. Each part had to be made with extreme accuracy to make sure that the whole could be fitted together without difficulty or delay. One of the tests which had to be passed by the completed guns involved disassembling five of them, scrambling the parts, and then reassembling them, without the use of tools, from parts chosen at random.

Despite the obvious difficulties involved in the manufacture of the howitzers, the company decided to submit a bid on an educational order for seventy guns, with deliveries to begin in 6 months at a rate of fourteen per month. When the bids of five manufacturers were opened, another company was found to have submitted a bid lower by about $50 per gun than the price asked by General Electric. The contract was awarded to the low bidder.

About 2 months later, however, the company which had received the contract concluded that it was unable to do the job, and the War Department asked General Electric to accept it. During these 2 months, however, the machine-tool builders who were to have supplied the rifling machines had become so loaded down with other orders that they could not make prompt delivery of the equipment General Electric needed. Army officials, however, urged the company to go ahead with the order as best it could.

The contract for 70 guns was signed Sept. 22, 1939, with deliveries to begin Feb. 12, 1940. Before this contract was completed a second contract was signed for 270 guns to be delivered at a rate of 20 per month. In September, 1940, came a third for 587, later increased to 618. This stepped up the production program to 35 guns a month. Another order for 360 caused a step-up to 50 guns a month. Additional con-

tracts for 140, 183, and 429 guns pushed the program to 70
per month. Even this speed proved inadequate. In the fall
of 1942, the War Department asked the company to expedite
deliveries beyond schedule. As a result 90 were turned out in
September, the same number in October, 100 in November,
and 90 in December.

The planning for the manufacture of the pack howitzer
involved 788 separate operations. It required 563 special jigs,
fixtures, and gauges and 332 special cutting tools. Although it
had been stated beforehand that a man with basic mathematical and mechanical experience would require 5 years
of special training to make howitzers successfully, the personnel of the Erie Works produced their first gun in approximately 6 months. Out of 2,070 complete guns and more than
300 extra tube assemblies only two were pronounced unac-
ceptable after proof firing. The original contract price was
practically cut in two on the final orders—due principally to
improved methods, greater skill, and less spoilage.

FROM ALASKA TO IRAN

All over the world, diesel-electric locomotives did a tremendous job of hauling materials and supplies for the armed
forces. The American Army had scarcely landed on the
beaches of Normandy before a diesel-electric locomotive
built at the Erie Works came rolling off an LST. Throughout
the war the Army was the biggest purchaser of these locomotives. Some were as small as 150 horsepower. Others were
as large as 1,000 horsepower. Hundreds of them were used in
the various theaters of operation from Alaska to Iran.

When the United States became an active participant in
the war, the Alaska Railroad had two headaches. Its salt-
water terminal at Seward, on Resurrection Bay, was too close
to the Japs. Its other port at Anchorage, on Cook Inlet, was
handicapped by a tremendous rise and fall of tide. So Congress authorized the construction of a 12-mile cutoff from the

Seward-Anchorage line to Whittier on comparatively safe Prince William Sound. This cutoff was completed in 1943 after boring two long tunnels and making many big fills. It shortened the distance between tidewater and the interior of Alaska by 50 miles and provided a more protected route for the transportation of vital war materials and supplies.

Joy over the construction of this new cutoff was soon cooled, however, by the discovery that the railroad's steam locomotives could not be operated over it. One tunnel was 13,000 feet long, the sixth longest tunnel in North America. The other was 4,911 feet long. In these long bores, smoke and gas from coal-burning steam locomotives endangered the lives of trainmen and passengers. To arrange adequate ventilation for these tunnels would have been extremely expensive and would have taken a long time.

The problem was solved when two Alco-G-E diesel-electric locomotives, each of 1,000 horsepower, were sent up from Schenectady to Alaska. They operated through the long tunnels without creating any smoke. Running as a pair, they were able to haul fifty-car trains over grades that would have limited steam locomotives to loads of twenty-five cars.

After the new locomotives had made their first trip, Col. O. A. Ohlson, general manager of the Alaska Railroad commented enthusiastically, "With no stops for water or cleaning the firebox, the operating costs will be less than for steam engines. If I ever get to the North Pole, like as not I'll be hauled by a diesel-electric—and I won't be surprised if it climbs right up the Pole!"

Halfway around the world in Iran, where 130-degree temperatures are common, a fleet of diesel-electric locomotives hauled millions of tons of food and ammunition for the U.S.S.R. from the Persian Gulf to Teheran. Equipped with special 1,600-gallon fuel tanks, they made the 650-mile run without stops through blistering sandstorms and over freezing mountains. Because of the little time required for servicing, these diesel-electric locomotives were able to remain on the job nearly 24 hours a day. Maintenance was so simple that their needs could be cared for adequately by natives trained and supervised by a few American Army railroaders.

THE WELDER-JEEP

On the battlefields of North Africa and Europe, and in the distant areas of the Southwest and the Central Pacific, emergency repair tools were almost as important as weapons. And the most widely needed repair tools for front-line equipment were welding sets. The sets used in World War I for the most part were heavy and cumbersome to transport, and were fairly difficult to use. With the tremendous increase in the number of tanks, tractors, trucks, guns, and other self-propelled vehicles in World War II, something more mobile than the old equipment was needed—a welding set that could be transported quickly and easily to the spot where the job was to be done.

To meet this need, a group of soldiers in an army repair unit stationed in Arizona proposed an ingenious idea. Why not install a generator and an electric arc welder in the right front seat of an ordinary, rough-and-ready jeep? Army engineers liked the suggestion so much that General Electric was given the job of designing a welding set for this purpose.

The result was a light, compact unit, operated by means of a belt connected to the engine of the jeep. As soon as the vehicle was brought to a stop, the apparatus was ready to go to work. In weight this welder-jeep was equivalent to a ¼-ton truck, whereas the equipment it replaced consisted of a 5-ton towing truck and a 1½-ton welding trailer. This weight reduction, plus the jeep's great maneuverability, enabled the unit to travel easily over rugged or muddy terrain where larger and heavier vehicles bogged down.

Before accepting the welder-jeep for service, the Army subjected it to rigid tests on a 500-mile obstacle course—the same as that used for combat tanks—and it came through with flying colors. The Army employed these units extensively in France and in the China-Burma-India theater of war, even transporting them at times by airplane. Because of their success, the Navy decided it had to have similar equipment for the LVT combat vehicle, commonly known as the "Alligator." The adaptability of the alligator-welder to the difficulties of landing operations made it of tremendous value in salvaging damaged equipment and getting it back into the fight with the greatest possible speed.

HOW TO HIDE THE PANAMA CANAL

Most people think of smoke screens in connection with the activities of the Navy. Their use, however, is by no means confined to concealment of vessels at sea. They are equally important to blind an enemy on land.

For a long time before World War II the United States Army had felt the need of an improved smoke-screen generator. Aid in this search was sought from Dr. Irving Langmuir, associate director of General Electric's Research Laboratory. He and his staff immediately went to work on the problem. They decided that the first thing to do was to determine definitely the most effective size, density, and color of smoke particles. After they had reached their conclusions as to what the particles should be like, the next problem was how to generate them in large quantities. Five different models of generators were built before one was found that would turn out the proper smoke particle, a liquid globule of microscopic proportions.

Known as the "M-1 Smoke Generator," this was a compact unit mounted on a rubber-tired trailer. It had three cubical tanks, joined together to look like one big box, containing sufficient smoke materials for long-time operation. In the middle was a small gasoline engine, and at the front a big cylindrical boiler, attached to which was a horizontal pipe with small vents for the discharge of the smoke. The whole thing looked something like an old-fashioned steam fire engine. While the design was developed at Schenectady, the actual making of the generators afterward was carried out by other manufacturers.

Before the development of the M-1, no method of smoke projection existed capable of large-area, daytime screening. But these generators were so effective that a small number of them correctly placed could mask an entire city—or even an area as great as the Panama Canal—from the eyes of attacking aircraft.

The invasion of Sicily and other later invasions were mounted with the aid of these smoke generators. Major General William N. Porter, chief of the Army's Chemical Warfare Service, was high in his praise of their performance. "Smoke is our greatest protective weapon," he said. "It is the greatest lifesaver of our troops and was responsible for the small number of casualties in Sicily."

A baby smoke generator, the M-2, was later developed by the Chemical Warfare Service utilizing the same principles that Doctor Langmuir worked out for the M-1. It was designed for use on jungle trails, at beachheads, and in foxholes. Small enough to be carried in the back seat of a jeep or similar vehicle, and weighing only 180 pounds, it was easily portable. In spite of its small size, however, this midget smoke generator could blot out an area 5 miles long and about 200 yards wide.

SECRET SHELL TO VANQUISH TANKS

As the war continued, the Nazis developed new and improved tanks, the Panther, the Tiger, and the Royal Tiger. They were bigger, carried larger guns, and were more heavily armored than their predecessors. Something had to be done to enable the Allies to match blows with these newest monsters.

Standing soldier loads rocket into rear end of a bazooka held by another soldier in kneeling position.

The folding bazooka shown at left was much handier in dense brush than the original model at right.

*Rocket launcher cluster under wing of a P-47 Thunder-
bolt—barrels made of plastics to save weight.*

*Rocket launchers mounted on tank—the entire frame-
work could be jettisoned after firing.*

*P-47 Thunderbolt in action—successive stages as rocket is fired
from launcher mounted under wing.*

One of the Army's most useful weapons, the 75-mm pack howitzer. Breech mechanisms being finished at Erie.

75-mm. howitzer in use on Guadalcanal. Manufacture of this weapon required 563 special jigs and 332 special cutting tools.

Welder jeep—a mobile unit for quick repair jobs near the front line. Generator is mounted alongside front seat.

G-E 25-ton diesel-electric locomotive operating over a newly repaired bridge in Germany.

Portable smoke generator of Chemical Warfare Service, principle for which was developed in the G.E. Research Laboratory.

Diesel-electric power for military railroads—locomotives under construction at the Erie Works.

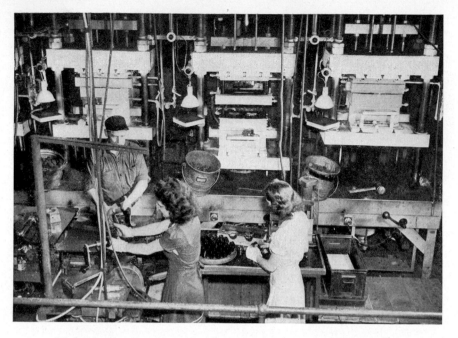

Making plastics fuses for the Army's 60-mm trench mortar.

Trench mortar in action. G.E. produced more than 26,000,000 plastics fuses for this weapon.

Production of a special armor-piercing shell was commenced in the summer of 1944 amid great secrecy. Actually, the new shell was a projectile within a projectile. Inside the assembly was a core of the hardest metal made by man—cemented tungsten carbide. This core was centered in a housing made mainly of aluminum. The primary function of the outer body was to streamline the shell and permit a smaller diameter armor-piercing core to be fired from a larger bore gun. For the 76-millimeter gun, for example, roughly half the weight was contained in the core. The total weight of the projectile was about 9 pounds, compared with roughly 15 pounds for conventional steel armor-piercing projectiles. As a result, the muzzle velocity of the new projectile was 3,400 feet per second compared with 2,800 feet per second for the conventional one. The cores for these shells were made by General Electric's affiliate, the Carboloy Company.

The new armor-piercing shells proved extremely effective in combating the big German tanks. The extreme hardness of the carbide prevented its being flattened out on impact. Specimens recovered after firing showed the nose of the carbide core to be virtually unmarked after having passed through several inches of armor plate. After penetration the core exploded into pieces, scattering in all directions inside the enemy tank.

Actually the combat effectiveness of these projectiles was even greater than was indicated by their greater armor-piercing ability. They were more accurate than ordinary shells, due in large part to their higher velocity and shorter flight time. With the new projectile it was possible to hit tanks in motion with much greater ease than formerly, while stationary targets could be hit with fewer misses even at long ranges. In the campaigns in France and the Rhineland the Germans relied heavily on their big tanks, but the new shell was too good for them. Time and again it was reported that a Nazi tank was put out of action with a single shot, sometimes at ranges as great as 3,000 yards.

FUSES FOR TRENCH MORTAR SHELLS

In connection with the Army's 60-millimeter trench-mortar shell, too, General Electric contributed an important development. This was a plastics fuse, the design of which was completed on the day before Pearl Harbor. These fuses had previously been made of aluminum. Their manufacture involved intricate close-tolerance metal machining. But, as a result of the widespread National Defense activity, screw machines for shaping, boring, and counterboring had become virtually unobtainable. Even if it had been possible to find the machines, it would have been impossible to train the necessary machinists quickly to operate them. And the Army needed the fuses in a hurry. Besides that, every available pound of aluminum was needed for aircraft.

The 60-millimeter trench mortar was an invaluable weapon because it was of simple construction and could be carried easily from place to place by the troops themselves. It was set up on a three-legged support with the barrel at a high angle. The shell was dropped in at the muzzle and allowed to slide down until it hit a firing pin at the bottom, which exploded the propulsion charge. The fuse did not function to set off the main charge until a pin, held by a strong string, had been released by the high acceleration developed when the shell left the mortar. Then, when the nose of the shell hit the target, the high explosive of the main charge was fired with devastating effect. Despite the development of many new weapons, these simple mortars, the doughboys' "portable artillery," were a vitally important part of the equipment of the infantry.

The shell from a trench mortar traveled at relatively low velocity. Since the barrel was not rifled, the shell did not spin during its flight. These factors made it possible to use for the fuse and nose a material that did not possess the extremely great strength required in a shell to be fired from a high-velocity, rifled gun. So Army Ordnance asked if the company could design and manufacture a nose of plastics.

Hundreds of experimental plastics fuses were laboriously made by hand. In actual firing tests these showed up as well as the original aluminum fuses, and the company received the "go-ahead" signal to put the plastics fuse in volume production. Copies were made of the original, intricate mold until a total of 105 molds were available, all alike. A new mechanized molding process was developed, different from anything that had ever been tried before, the plastics mortar fuses began coming off the production line by the thousands.

Everything went smoothly until December, 1944, when the Germans staged their startling break-through in the Ardennes. The American armies had been using about 1,300,000 trench-mortar shells a month before the break-through. General Eisenhower asked that this number be doubled immediately. The Pittsfield Plastics Plant, because of an acute man-power shortage, was already experiencing difficulty in keeping up with its production schedule. So the company rented some factory space that was available at Holyoke and established a new plant there devoted entirely to the making of trench-mortar fuses. The new plant got into production in record time and production was stepped up so effectively that the Ordnance Department sent the company a special letter of commendation for its achievement.

Every one of the 26 million plastics mortar fuses that the company turned out during the war saved a pound of aluminum. The aluminum fuses had cost upwards of a dollar apiece. Long before the end of the war General Electric was turning out the plastics fuses at a cost of only 25 cents apiece. At the same time there was a tremendous saving of scrap. For the first 20 million fuses shipped, the tonnage of plastics scrap amounted to only 3.48 per cent of the total tonnage. Accuracy of manufacture was extremely high. The Army found it necessary to reject only two-tenths of 1 per cent of all the fuses shipped.

11

Power Plants on the Fighting Fronts

BECAUSE OF THE EXTENSIVE USE of electricity on shipboard and the large amounts of generating equipment needed to supply it, ships were often described as "floating power-houses." This characterization was sometimes even more apt than was intended. On more than one occasion a ship's generators were called into service to supply power on land.

SAVING THE DAY AT CHERBOURG

When a stand-by electric-power plant at the captured French port of Cherbourg broke down in August, 1944, its failure threatened the Allied advance down the Normandy peninsula. For this drive enormous amounts of supplies were needed, and Cherbourg was the only port available. Without electric power, port operations there were desperately handicapped.

Before the occupation of the port by the Americans, power for the Cherbourg area had come from a central generating station at Caen, 45 miles away. The Germans destroyed the high-voltage transmission line when they withdrew, leaving only an old local stand-by plant of small capacity. First one and then the other of its two small generators burned out.

A survey showed the windings of the generators to be

completely destroyed. French engineers estimated that repairs would take at least 2 months and maybe longer. Nothing but a few small diesel-driven generator sets were available as substitutes.

Rear Admiral John Wilkes of the U.S. Navy then recalled how the great aircraft carrier *Lexington* had once supplied the city of Tacoma, Wash., with power from her main-drive generators during an emergency. He knew that the electric-drive destroyer escort U.S.S. *Donnell* was lying idle in a British port. Sixty feet of her stern had been blown off a short time before by a German torpedo, but her 4,600-kilowatt G-E generators were in good working order. Why not, he thought, try the same hookup at Cherbourg that had been so successful at Tacoma?

To do this was not quite as simple as it seemed. It was easy enough to tow the destroyer escort across the Channel and moor her in Cherbourg harbor, but the electrical system in the Cherbourg area was designed for 5,000 volts 50 cycles, while the ship's generators were designed to operate at 2,700 volts 93⅓ cycles. By slowing down the *Donnell's* equipment the desired frequency could be obtained, but that meant a voltage drop to 1,500. To bring this up somewhere near the 5,000-volt level of the Cherbourg distribution system it was necessary to find a transformer with a 3 to 1 step-up.

Only one undamaged transformer could be found in the whole Cherbourg area. This was a German-built unit overlooked in the Nazis' last minute campaign of destruction. No one knew its rating. French engineers thought it had been used to bring down the 33,000-volt transmission line from Caen to the 5,000-volt local distribution level—a 6 to 1 step-down unit. The only hope of being able to use it lay in locating a midtap and changing the connections for use as a step-up unit.

The transformer was opened, and a sigh of relief went up from the engineers when they found a midtap just where it was needed. The *Donnell* was warped up to the dock and lines were run to the transformer. Other lines were run to tie into the distribution system. Despite hasty improvisation, the hookup worked, and the *Donnell* carried the whole power load of the Cherbourg area without a hitch until the middle of December when the old stand-by plant was ready to take over again.

OTHER "SHIP-TO-SHORE" INSTALLATIONS

Even before the *Donnell* lighted the captured city of Cherbourg, the Navy and General Electric had been working together on the idea of "ship-to-shore" power hookups. Thorough investigation had been made of the possibilities of equipping electric-drive vessels with conversion equipment suitable for supplying power from propulsion generators to land installations. It was decided that destroyer escorts were the most suitable type of vessel for this purpose and fifteen of them were selected for the job.

Studies were made of the operating voltages in the various theaters where it was thought likely that emergency electric power supplies might be needed. Each ship was then provided with a totally enclosed deck-mounted substation consisting of a transformer, switchgear, and water-cooling equipment. The apparatus was so designed that power could be supplied at any one of six voltages ranging from 2,400 to 37,500.

When Gen. Douglas MacArthur's victorious Yanks pushed into the city of Manila in the closing days of February, 1945, they found that more than 2,000 blocks of the once-glittering city had been destroyed, along with bridges, docks, the power system, and a large part of the street railways. Following a landing on the tip of the Bataan peninsula, and a paratrooper descent on Corregidor, Manila Bay was cleared. Then a "ship-to-shore" equipped destroyer escort moved in and anchored about 300 yards off shore. Power cables were laid on floats from the vessel to the land, and the big generators began to hum.

Electric lights shone once more in the battered city. Elevators began to run. Reconstruction work was started—helped by the most useful of all man's tools, electric power.

GENERATING UNITS ON BARGES

Following the job done by the U.S.S. *Lexington* at Tacoma, Wash., in 1929, the Public Service Company of New Hampshire placed the power ship *Jacona* in commission in 1930. This floating generating station utilized the hull of an old, 400-foot, cargo ship built for World War I. It had been retired from service and was destined for scrapping when the idea was born of converting it into a floating power plant. Propulsion machinery was removed, and in its place two General Electric 10,000-kilowatt turbine-generators were installed along with boiler equipment, fuel tanks, transformers, and the necessary switchgear.

The *Jacona's* first assignment was to carry the power load of a newly built paper mill at Bucksport, Me., pending the construction of a permanent powerhouse. Later she was moved to a location on the Piscataqua River near Portsmouth, N.H., where she furnished power to a near-by substation on land. In this location she performed a useful service for a long period. During the latter part of the war she was used at Pearl Harbor.

With war clouds hovering on the horizon in 1941, the Army began to worry about means to ensure continuity of power supply for plants engaged in defense work. It was felt that trouble might arise from natural causes, or, in the event of war, by deliberate destruction of generating stations by bombing or sabotage.

To provide against such dangers, engineers of General Electric proposed an adaptation of the *Jacona* scheme—the construction of a number of floating power stations of 30,-

000-kilowatt capacity. A study of the various coastal and inland waterways indicated that the maximum dimensions permissible for such craft would be a length of 300 feet, a beam of 50 feet, and a draft of 9 feet. So constructed they could navigate the Ohio and Mississippi rivers to reach Pittsburgh, Cincinnati, St. Louis, Memphis, and New Orleans. They could be towed through the Illinois River to Chicago and then into the Great Lakes to Milwaukee, Detroit, Cleveland, Erie, and Buffalo. In addition to being able to navigate the major inland waterways, the barges would be able to skirt the Atlantic Coast for service at Eastern seaboard cities.

Each barge was equipped with a 30,000-kilowatt hydrogen-cooled turbine-generator and two marine-type high-pressure boilers designed for burning either gas or oil. Sufficient fuel for preliminary operation was carried in a double bottom. In this space were also a number of ballast tanks, which could be filled with or emptied of water to lower or raise the vessel as conditions of navigation might demand. The stacks were removable so that the barge could clear low bridges in transit.

Four of these floating power plants were built, the first complete unit being delivered in May, 1943. Their names were *Resistance, Reactance, Inductance,* and *Sea Power.* After being assembled at a shipyard near Pittsburgh, Pa., each barge was given a thorough test by being hooked up to the power system of the Duquesne Light Company. All performed in a satisfactory manner. Shortly after its completion, one of these units was put to work at Pensacola, Fla., when a serious power shortage developed in that city.

How to make the most advantageous use of the others was something of a problem. Critical power shortages never developed in the United States, as had been feared. Then an unforeseen situation presented itself. As the Allied drive progressed toward Berlin, Cherbourg became inadequate to handle the huge volume of supplies crossing the Channel from England. The great Belgian port of Antwerp, evacuated by the Germans, was much nearer than Cherbourg to the fighting front, but could not be put to use effectively without an adequate supply of electric power.

It was suggested that one or two of the big floating power plants be sent across the Atlantic. Sailors shook their heads in doubt. The barges had been built for use on quiet, inland waterways. Lacking propulsion equipment, they had to be towed from place to place. To tow them across the ocean would be an extremely difficult task. Their draft was so shallow that they would be hopelessly unseaworthy, the sailors said, in the stormy waters of the North Atlantic.

Nevertheless it was decided to make the attempt. The *Resistance* was equipped with a bow section and arrangements were made for her to be towed across the ocean by the Army Transportation Corps under the vigilant eyes of a Navy convoy. Despite advance misgivings the voyage was successfully accomplished. Averaging a speed of 3 knots, and bobbing around like a cork, the craft took 51 days to make the crossing.

No enemy activity was encountered at sea or in the English Channel. But, as the convoy entered the mouth of the estuary of the Scheldt River at dusk it was attacked by a pack of U-boats. A running fight continued all night, but the *Resistance* came through unharmed. By daybreak the convoy had reached safety some distance up stream from the mouth of the estuary. Off Antwerp the huge floating power plant was connected to lines of the Belgian distribution system, and that great port began to receive power from the ship's turbine-generators.

Although the Germans had done what they could to destroy Antwerp when they departed, they did not relax their efforts on leaving. For months afterward they poured a steady stream of V-bombs into the city. More than 2,600 of them arrived during the period when the *Resistance* was furnishing power to the city, but the barge remained unharmed.

Later, another of these units, the *Sea Power*, was towed across and supplied power at Rotterdam. A third went to Manila after the recapture of that city. Employment of the floating electric-generating stations overseas was far from the idea in mind when they were designed, yet proved to be a material aid in the conduct of the war.

RAILROAD POWER PLANTS FOR THE NAVY

One of the Navy's most unusual war-emergency units neither sailed through the water nor flew through the air, but, paradoxically, did its traveling on railroad tracks. It was a mobile power plant mounted on a train of six especially built cars.

Like the floating power plants designed for operation on inland waterways, the power train was intended to furnish current in emergencies to plants engaged in the production of war material. Two of these trains were ordered from General Electric in the summer of 1941.

While the basic idea was simple enough, the difficulties involved in design and construction were by no means easy to overcome. First of all, equipment had to be designed within the limiting clearances on major railroads. Secondly, it had to be so placed on the cars that the allowable axle loads were not exceeded. Nothing of the kind had ever been made before. A large number of mobile substations had been built, but never a large mobile generating station.

Careful study indicated that a capacity of 10,000 kilowatts was the maximum practicable size for a unit of this kind. It was decided that a complete train should consist of six cars, one for the boiler, one for the turbine-generator, one for switchgear, one for transformers, and two for pumps and auxiliary equipment. Special cars had to be built. Those for the boilers and turbines were the largest and heaviest railroad cars ever designed for use in America. The boiler car was 88 feet long and weighed 430,000 pounds; the turbine car was 86 feet long and weighed 540,000 pounds. To avoid excessive axle load the car was supported on four trucks with a total of ten axles. With this arrangement it was possible to operate the trains at speeds up to 40 miles an hour.

One of these mobile power plants was stationed at the Philadelphia Navy Yard, available for emergencies in the Eastern or Central States. For a considerable period it was used at Jacksonville, Fla. The second unit was stationed at San Francisco. Although the necessity for great haste did not actually arise, engineers estimated that the plants could have made steam and been put on the line within 24 hours after arrival at the scene of service.

POWER TRAINS FOR SOVIET DRIVE TO BERLIN

Experience gained in the construction of power trains for the Navy proved of immense value later when the company received an order for sixty-three mobile power plants for the U.S.S.R. These were similar in principle to the American units, but different in detail. Forty were of 3,000-kilowatt capacity and twenty-three of 1,000-kilowatt capacity.

Each train consisted of ten cars. One car carried the turbine-generator. Each of two cars mounted a locomotive-type boiler, automatically stoked for poor grades of fuel such as lignite. Two other cars carried water for use where no local supply was available. In addition there was a switchgear car, a crew car, and three radiator cars for water cooling.

In the wide-open spaces of the U.S.S.R. there are many locations where water is scarce. For that reason it was necessary to provide not only tank cars to supply the water but also cooling cars to permit its re-use. Otherwise, the power train would have been such a water-hog that its employment would have been impossible in many places.

As the Soviet army advanced after lifting the long siege

of Stalingrad, it faced unprecedented problems of supply in an area twice scorched to desolation, first in its own retreat and again when the Germans were pulling out. So wide was the swath of ruin that it was virtually impossible to send damaged front-line equipment all the way back to repair shops in the far rear. Repair facilities had to follow the army closely, and electric power was necessary to operate them.

"Without electricity," commented Lt. Gen. L. G. Rudenko after the delivery of these mobile power plants, "one finds oneself quite helpless, and it takes weeks, sometimes months, to rebuild power stations. If the railroads have not been destroyed we can now have power within 24 hours. And if they have, new rails can be laid in a short time."

The mobile power plants helped to restore Stalingrad, the Donbas, the Crimea, Zaporozhe, Krivoi Rog, Gomel, Minsk, and other cities. For locations to which transmission lines could be run from existing power stations, General Electric built a number of 1,800 kva railroad-mounted substations.

Altogether the company produced during the war a total of 283,000 kilowatts of generating capacity in floating and railroad-mounted power plants. This equipment was roughly the amount of generating apparatus necessary to meet the normal needs of a million people.

DIESEL-OPERATED POWER PLANTS

The struggle in the Pacific involved the taking, holding, and operation of a series of Naval bases extending from Pearl Harbor to Tokyo. Generators engineered and built by General Electric supplied power to most of these bases.

Immediately after Pearl Harbor the Navy began ordering completely self-contained, 600-kilowatt, portable power plants, diesel-engine driven and mounted on rubber-tired trailers. The Erie Works, accustomed to building diesel-electric locomotives, assembled a diesel engine with a Fort Wayne Works generator in the cab of a locomotive. Philadelphia Works supplied the switchgear. The cab contained all the switches, voltage regulators, and controls that were ordinarily used in the conventional power plant. The customary locomotive driving gear was, of course, omitted.

The result was that this portable power-plant trailer looked very much like an electric locomotive, except that it was fitted with rubber-tired wheels. It could be hauled to the place where it was to be used, jacked up, and put in operation at once. Up to the time the war ended the company had supplied fifty of these units.

The first two units to be assembled were sent to Pearl Harbor where they supplied the power to run the machinery for pumping out the battleships and other warships sunk in the surprise attack there. Others were used at Guam, Okinawa, Tinian, Saipan, Cavite, and Subic Bay. Sometimes they were operated individually and sometimes in groups.

Because of the nature of the equipment it was thought that the Navy personnel would not be sufficiently familiar with its handling, setting up, and operation. The Navy, therefore, asked that a special training school be established at Erie to teach selected groups of Seabee and other Navy personnel how these jobs should be done. The schedule provided for about 60 hours of instruction equally divided between classroom and factory. An instruction manual was supplied to each student covering all the various aspects of the subject. More than 100 men were graduated from these courses. Later these men supervised the installation and operation of the units.

Reports from the field told of the excellent performance of these portable power plants. "The units run remarkably well," said one. "They stood up at Okinawa under that terrific hurricane which wrecked ships and completely ruined practically all small equipment."

One of the men who had taken the special instruction

course wrote back, "My crew has been busy the past two weeks training Army men so that they can take over the operation of our units, as we are to move on and build another system. The new men are as thoroughly sold on the units as we were, so they will be in good hands."

12

Radar—the Magic Eye

RADAR, THE ALL-SEEING ELECTRIC EYE, is credited with having contributed more to the success of the United Nations in World War II than did any other single device. It turned the tide in the Battle of Britain. It gave the hard-pressed American Navy a priceless advantage over the Japanese while our new ships were under construction. It won the battle of the Atlantic against the German submarines. These achievements in the dark hours when defeat might have meant the loss of the war were actually the margin of ultimate victory.

The art of "radio detection and ranging," from which the name "radar" came, was not a sudden startling discovery. Long before the war scientists had discovered that a radio wave directed at a solid object would be reflected back to its source in the same way that a sound wave is reflected back as an echo. Development of this idea was carried out independently in various parts of the world. During the 1930's, England, France, Germany, and the United States all evolved fairly successful detection devices based on the principle that an unseen object could be forced to reveal itself by causing a radio echo.

RADIOLOCATION IN THE BATTLE OF BRITAIN

Out of Britain's vulnerability to air attack came the first extensive operational radar system. A chain of five "radiolocation" stations for detecting the approach of hostile aircraft was secretly established on the east coast of England in 1935. Two years later, fifteen more stations were added to the chain, giving complete coverage of the whole east and southeast coasts from Scotland to the Isle of Wight. Beginning in the spring of 1939, a 24-hour radar watch was kept at all these stations. In this way Britain was protected by a curtain of radar waves, hundreds of miles in extent, which no aircraft could penetrate undetected. Not even the British public knew of the existence of this radar curtain, so well was the secret kept.

Assaults on England by the *Luftwaffe* began on Aug. 8, 1940. Day after day for 6 weeks the German airforce attacked without mercy. Day after day the small Royal Air Force met each thrust and beat it back with terrific loss. How did they do it? They did not have enough planes to maintain a constant patrol in the air. A handful of small, fast, hard-hitting fighters had to be pitted against the entire bomber force of Germany. These fighters did not have sufficient time to get off the ground after the enemy raiders were seen approaching the coast at a speed of 200 miles an hour, yet they were always ready when the *Luftwaffe* came over.

The Germans thought the English must be gifted with second sight to tell them just when and where each blow was coming. And so they were—the second sight provided by the magic electric eye of radar, which gave warning when the attackers were still a long distance away.

During the fateful month of August the average loss of the *Luftwaffe* in raids over England was 15 per cent. The total loss was 957 planes of all sorts. On September 15, often said to have been the turning point in the Battle of Britain, the Germans lost 185 aircraft out of 500 which attacked. Without radar the bombers could have dropped their explosives and started home before the British fighters could attack.

EARLY AMERICAN DEVELOPMENTS

Until then radar development in the United States had been largely on an experimental basis. Back in 1922, Dr. A. Hoyt Taylor of the Naval Research Laboratory, and his associate, Leo C. Young, had discovered accidentally that the transmission of radio waves across the Potomac River was affected by the passing of a small steamer. This suggested the possibility of using radio to detect the presence of enemy vessels. Later experiments by these same men showed that reflections of radio waves from an airplane could be similarly detected.

At this time General Electric engineers, too, were working on the problem of aircraft detection. During World War I, sound detection was used to pick up planes, with the aid of large listening horns. As plane speeds increased, however, sound was no longer fast enough to give adequate warning. The planes would arrive almost as soon as the sound waves revealed their presence. In 1928, one of the company's engineers, Dr. E. F. W. Alexanderson, devised a method of obtaining the altitude of an airplane above the ground by directing a radio beam downward and picking up its reflection. Experiments were extended to the detection of planes with radio waves about a meter in length. Another series of tests was conducted by Chester W. Rice, in the company's Engineering General Division, using radio waves between 1 and 10 centimeters long. Automobiles on a near-by road were picked up at a distance of a mile and a quarter, and a small open Waco biplane at a distance of a mile.

At the same time the company's Research Laboratory and Radio Department were active in the fields of radio communication and television, particularly in the development of a wide variety of electronic tubes including the "magnetron," the high-vacuum tube, the four-element tube, and the gas-filled rectifier tube. In many respects radar is closely related to television. Experience in this field was extremely helpful in enabling the company to tackle the radar problem quickly and deliver complete units within a few months when the U.S. Navy called for equipment.

American radar developments had been rather loosely coordinated before 1940. Organization of the National Defense Research Committee—later to become part of the Office of Scientific Research and Development—in the summer of that year was an important step in unifying research and development activities on radar. Shortly afterward, a British technical mission came to the United States, and mutual disclosures were made of British and American accomplishments in radar up to that time. Thereafter the efforts of both countries were combined. To expedite development the Radiation Laboratory was set up by the NDRC at the Massachusetts Institute of Technology, staffed by physicists from a number of universities.

START OF LARGE-SCALE PRODUCTION

The increasing likelihood of American participation in the war demanded large-scale production of radar equipment. So urgent was the need that General Electric took the drastic step of dropping all commercial radio development work and concentrating wholly on government needs. In the spring of 1941 the Navy signed a contract with the company for the manufacture of 400 sets of "early-warning" radar for use on shipboard. This equipment employed a high-frequency pulse system in which very short impulses were sent out at brief intervals followed by periods of rest during which the incoming "echo" from the target was received. Under this arrangement it was possible to have transmitter and receiver at the same location, which had been impossible with earlier designs.

The first of these sets were installed on a group of ten destroyers in November, 1941. As no equipment of this type had previously been used on American combat ships, the company was asked to furnish a group of twelve engineers to supervise the installation of the equipment, instruct the vessels' officers, technicians, and operators in its operation and maintenance, and service the gear when the ships returned to bases after periods of active service.

Tact and judgment were often needed by these field engineers in dealing with the captains of the vessels on which radar was installed. The officers had never used such equipment before and did not know what it could do. It occupied considerable space. Its installation frequently required structural changes in the vessel. And if, as sometimes happened, it encroached on the skipper's private quarters, this newfangled device was regarded with a noticeable lack of enthusiasm. But this attitude soon changed. Captains who would have pitched the stuff overboard if they had been free to follow their own first inclinations became loud in their praise of it.

In the spring of 1942, a slightly modified type of equipment made its appearance. Six months later two other models came into production, one being especially designed for the Navy's largest ships. These were followed from time to time by additional improved models. Altogether the company turned out nearly 1,500 of these locator sets. They assisted a weakened Navy in making maximum use of its limited number of vessels in the period immediately after Pearl Harbor. They enabled a much more powerful Navy ultimately to carry the war boldly into Japanese home waters.

COMBATTING THE SUBMARINE MENACE

At the beginning of the war Germany decided to make a major effort to destroy Allied shipping by concentrated sub-

marine warfare. Her main object was to halt the flow of materials and men across the North Atlantic, though destruction
in other areas was also included in the plan. The U-boat rated
top priority in Nazi war production. By 1942, Germany had
a fleet of nearly 700 submarines and was sinking Allied ships
at a rate of 16,000 tons a day. Proudly, Admiral Doenitz pro-
claimed that "The enemy possesses no means of defense
against our U-boats."

But new and effective means of combatting the submarine
were in the making. The Navy had developed a new type of
ship—the destroyer escort—that could overhaul, outmaneu-
ver, and outshoot the U-boat. The Army Air Forces had organized the 1st Sea-search Attack Group. Provided with the
latest types of radar these ships and planes began a relent-
less "hunt-and-kill" campaign against the U-boats.

A submarine relies for protection on its ability to conceal
itself under water, but it cannot stay there indefinitely. In
the days before radar it could get along comfortably, even
in hostile waters, by remaining submerged during the day
and coming to the surface at night to take on fresh air and
charge batteries. But there is no night in radar's world. A surfaced submarine can be detected just as easily in the darkness as in the light.

When Allied ships and planes began a systematic radar
hunt for submarines, life became distinctly uncomfortable
for the U-boats. They found themselves under attack whenever they attempted to remain on the surface for any considerable period of time, and the attacks came so swiftly
that there was no opportunity to escape by diving under
water.

A temporary respite was gained for the U-boats when the
Germans captured a British "air to surface vessel" radar set
and then equipped their submarines with special listening
devices, which enabled them to tell when they were in an
area being swept by radar. As soon as they found that they

were in such an area, they protected themselves by submerging.

This respite did not last long. A new type of short-wave radar took the place of the older types. The Germans tried desperately to develop a new receiver to detect this short-wave searching, but met with little success. During May, June, and July of 1943, nearly 100 confirmed U-boat kills were made. Shipping losses declined steadily. By the summer of 1944, President Roosevelt and Prime Minister Churchill were able to announce in a joint statement that the submarine had become the hunted rather than the hunter. "They have been attacked from the Arctic to the Pacific, aircraft playing a great part. The number of U-boats sunk now exceeds 500." As radar was still a secret weapon at that time, no mention could be made of the part it had played, but the men of the Navy and the Air Forces knew, and the Germans had more than a suspicion of it.

Before the war was over General Electric participated in the design and manufacture of more than fifty different kinds of radar sets for the armed services, including air-borne equipment, long-range units for aircraft carriers, and huge mobile units for the Army, each requiring a fleet of seven trucks for its transportation. In some instances the design was entirely the work of the company's own engineers—in others the design was developed elsewhere and the company's only responsibility was the manufacture of the equipment. In some instances the company was the only supplier; at other times the manufacturing responsibility was divided. In many instances the company made some components of a particular set while the rest were made by others. All in all, radar production was a tremendous job—one of the biggest of the company's war assignments, amounting in terms of money in the neighborhood of a half-million dollars a day!

RADAR COUNTERMEASURES

Radar, along with its many excellent attributes as a weapon of war, had one notable weakness. An electrical "sound," like an ordinary sound, had to be sent out in great volume to produce even a relatively weak echo. That had obvious disadvantages. An operating radar continuously advertised its presence to anyone who might be listening. Moreover, so weak an echo could quite easily be drowned out by properly arranged interference.

After radar's first great success in the Battle of Britain it had seemed that the Allies possessed an unbeatable means of detecting enemy movements. Then the Germans devised a system of radar interference that so jammed the Allies' equipment that the German battleships *Gneisenau* and *Scharnhorst* were able to navigate the English Channel safely under its cover. Something had to be done, and done quickly. The answer was found in changing to a new type of short-wave radar less susceptible to interference.

In the United States, as a result of this experience, the Army and Navy asked the National Defense Research Committee to undertake a study of the whole field of radar interference and countermeasures. For this purpose the committee organized Division 15 under the leadership of Dr. C. G. Suits, who later became director of General Electric's Research Laboratory. Headquarters were established at Schenectady. Laboratories located in other cities also contributed. The original staff numbered about 200 but in a short time it grew to more than 800. One reason why the Allies achieved their victory as quickly as they did was that they were always one step ahead of the enemy in counterradar activities.

Countermeasures to knock out German radar were used with considerable success before the Allied landing in Sicily. They greatly reduced British and American losses during air attacks on Germany. On D Day they proved of tremendous value in protecting the Allied landings in France.

Early in the war the Germans, preparing to meet Allied air attacks, gave highest priority to the manufacture of antiaircraft weapons. When the conflict reached a critical stage, their key areas were defended by the greatest concentration of antiaircraft artillery and radar in the history of warfare. Altogether, they had a total of about 16,000 heavy guns and 4,000 Wurzburg-type radar sets capable of tracking aircraft with a precision approaching that obtained with optical control. These defenses were able to exact heavy toll of Allied planes when concentrated bombing of German cities was begun.

The first step to upset this scheme of defense was the dropping of long strips of metallic foil known by the code word "Window." The air crews called it "Chaff." These strips, cut to a length appropriate to the frequency of the radar being countered, sent back an appreciable radar echo. A few thousand such strips with a total weight of less than 2 ounces, falling freely through the air, gave an echo as strong as that of a bomber. Masses of Window produced an effect like a squadron of airplanes.

When Window was first used by the British during a raid on Hamburg in July, 1943, spectacular results were obtained. Losses were cut to a small fraction of those sustained in earlier attacks. Nazi radar operators were overheard to exclaim in dismay, "The planes are doubling themselves." Even when the Germans found out what was happening, as they did very quickly, there was nothing they could do about it. They knew they were getting fake echoes on their radar receivers, but, in the general confusion, they couldn't distinguish the fake from the real.

Meanwhile the American Army Air Forces were working on the development of an electronic radar-jamming device called "Carpet." The theory of Carpet was simply to produce a continuous electric "noise" that drowned out the echoes returning to the German radar receivers.

Special electronic tubes were needed for these jammers, and the General Electric Research Laboratory had a large part in their development. Back in 1921, Dr. Albert W. Hull had invented a new tube called the "magnetron," which, it was found, could be used to produce radio waves of very high frequency, like those employed in radar, and of considerable power. To meet the needs of the jammers, the laboratory developed a complete line of somewhat similar magnetrons of high power covering a wide range of frequencies.

Produced in record time, the jamming equipment was flown to England and installed on planes of two U.S. heavy bombardment groups. In October, 1943, during an American raid on the city of Bremen, the Germans got their first taste of the new jamming technique. About 80 per cent of the German radar-controlled antiaircraft batteries were jammed out of operation. As a result, the Carpet-equipped planes suffered losses less than half those of the nonequipped planes.

The General Engineering Laboratory developed and built fifty wide-range oscillators for jammer transmitters in 4 months for the U.S. Navy and three wide-range direct-reading wavemeters for the Research Laboratory in 3 months.

By the end of the war, practically every American heavy bomber was using both Window and Carpet. A statement by one of Germany's well-known scientists was to the effect that:

The dispensing of "Doppel" in conjunction with the simultaneous application of electronic jamming produces such catastrophic results that the attack is by preference tracked with optical means and therefore our defense is practically blind. The awful destruction of our cities which the enemy oftentimes carries out with negligible losses is an eloquent proof of the effectiveness of these jamming means used by the enemy.

So desperate was the situation that almost every German expert on high-frequency radio was frantically trying to de-

vise an antijamming device for the Wurzburg radar. A public competition was held to discover a means to prevent or
counteract jamming. Despite the offer of tremendous prizes,
no satisfactory solution of the problem was found.

Against the Japanese, radar countermeasures were equally
effective. One memorable Saturday in the fall of 1944 representatives of the Navy came to the General Electric Research
Laboratory with an urgent request for a new electronic tube
to operate in a jamming transmitter at a frequency different
from the magnetron then in use. This was needed in the
Pacific where Jap torpedo bombers with radar equipment
had just made their appearance. Ten of the new jammers
plus spares were wanted for installation on battleships within
a week.

Experiments were started at once looking to the development of a tube of this kind. Fortunately it was found that
the tube previously used could be redesigned to have the
proper characteristics. In addition to the tubes, however,
other parts were needed. These included new antennas keyed
to the new frequency, transmission lines, dummy antennas to
tune the equipment without creating a signal, and transmitter modification parts.

Equipment for the entire ten sets was ready on the morning of the ninth day after the request was received. That
afternoon they were picked up by a Navy transport plane
and headed for the Pacific. A short time later they were in
operation under actual battle conditions.

Guided by radar, a Japanese plane would fly toward an
American warship. Watchful eyes followed its progress on
the ship's own radar. When the bomber was close enough to
indicate which particular ship was the intended target, the
countermeasures operators on that ship would turn on the
jammer. Then, on their radar screen, they could see the Jap
waver and finally turn back, his radar having failed him at
the critical moment. The battleship *North Carolina* actually

turned back three Japanese attacks on the day after the new jamming equipment was installed.

The story of radar in the war was a story of a race against time. Whatever some scientists did, other scientists tried to undo. In this race the American and British scientists far outdistanced the Germans and Japanese. It can be truly said that the United Nations had radar and made the most of it; the Axis also had radar, but, because of Allied countermeasures, got very little out of it.

13

Making Gunfire More Effective

THE SPECTACULAR SUCCESS OF RADAR in providing early warning of enemy aircraft in the Battle of Britain tended at first to freeze the thinking about radar along those lines. As the war progressed, however, it was discovered that radar had broader possibilities.

BATTLE OF THE BUZZ BOMBS

When a modern gun fails to hit the target, the fault is usually with the aiming. Guns are manufactured with such precision that the margin of error in their performance is extremely small, while the opportunity for error in aiming is much greater. A high-flying airplane is hard to see under the best conditions. To find its range by optical means is always difficult and sometimes impossible. But the wartime development of radar provided a means of aiming antiaircraft guns quickly and accurately at distant, fast-moving targets. This was the key to the Allies' success in beating the Nazis' much talked-of, secret weapon, the *Vergeltungswaffe-eins*, V-1, or buzz bomb.

Long before the actual dawn of D Day the Germans knew that an Allied invasion of France was being planned. So they, in turn, planned a kind of counterinvasion—the bombing of

England by pilotless aircraft. Hints of this intention, gained by Allied intelligence, gave an idea of what the Nazis had in mind, but there was little that could be done to prevent it.

The Allied air forces tried to smash the launching sites for these pilotless aircraft, or buzz bombs, but they met with small success. The sites were difficult to find from the air. They were small and hard to hit when found. Most discouragingly, they were not easily damaged even by a direct hit. Nevertheless, the air forces smothered them with bombs whenever they could be located, and this probably delayed the opening of the German attack.

Meanwhile defensive measures were being taken in England. A line of balloons connected by nets was set up across the Downs. Every British city that could spare a balloon contributed. The coastal-warning radar system was improved. The latest types of fighter planes—fast enough to catch the buzz bombs—were mobilized. New antiaircraft artillery was made ready.

Then the buzz bombs came. The balloon barrage caught a few of them. Mostly they went over its top or through the spaces between the wires. Coastal radar gave warning, but the air force, organized to cope with intensive raids of limited duration, found great difficulty in coping with raids of moderate intensity that continued ceaselessly. Moreover, the raids went on during all kinds of weather and part of the time the defending fighters could only sit helplessly on the ground and listen to the buzz bombs passing unseen overhead. It very quickly became apparent that if the bombs were to be stopped at all, the antiaircraft artillery would have to do it.

A year earlier this would have been an impossible assignment. But the antiaircraft batteries defending England now had some new, American-designed equipment: radar gun directors. These not only located the approaching buzz bombs, but gave complete position data—range, azimuth, and elevation—with an error of less than 25 feet in 18 miles. These data were transmitted automatically to the gun directors for gun positioning and fire control. The gun crew didn't have to hear or see the bomb. Radar tracked it for them and told them exactly where the target was.

It was the most effective defense against air attack that the world had ever seen. On one particular day 105 buzz bombs crossed the British coast headed for London. Only three of them arrived. Antiaircraft artillery was shooting them out of the air at a rate of one bomb downed for every forty rounds fired. The Germans were utterly frustrated. They simply could not afford to go on with the enormous effort the buzz bombs represented, when so few of them were accomplishing anything.

Development of radar control of antiaircraft artillery had been a lengthy process. The first experimental apparatus was built at the Radiation Laboratory at the Massachusetts Institute of Technology. Then, in the fall of 1941, the National Defense Research Committee asked General Electric for a production model. While this development was still in progress, the company's engineers started work on a modified design that was quickly adopted by the Army and became widely known as the "SCR-584." This was a mobile portable unit contained in a single trailer, while the sets previously employed for the same purpose had always required several vehicles to transport the equipment.

It was first used at the Anzio beachhead in February, 1944. Later it was employed for a variety of purposes by both the Army and the Marine Corps. Besides its use for antiaircraft fire control, it served as an early-warning radar against approaching enemy aircraft and as a ground control for low-flying fighter aircraft in the drive across France. In the Italian campaign it was used to detect the movement of road transportation.

800,000,000-CANDLEPOWER SEARCHLIGHTS

While radar control of antiaircraft guns was still in the development stage, visual aiming had to be employed. Sound locators were used for advance warning and searchlights for night spotting. Everyone living near the seacoast of the United States during the war became familiar with the sight of the powerful beams of these searchlights sweeping across the night sky. In the vicinity of a large city it was not unusual to see as many as a dozen of them at one time.

Antiaircraft searchlights were first used in World War I, but only to a limited extent. Many improvements in design were worked out during the period between wars, culminating in a monster 60-inch design rated at 800,000,000 candlepower. So powerful were these lights that a person could easily read a newspaper in an airplane at night at a distance of 12 miles from the source of light.

Entry of the United States into World War II stepped up demands for these searchlights to unprecedented levels. Early in 1942, the company's air-conditioning department at Bloomfield stopped all work on oil- and gas-fired boilers and furnaces for residential and commercial use, and converted its facilities to searchlight manufacture. The production job continued for 2 years and was completed early in 1944, when 1,197 searchlights had been built.

At Erie the last household refrigerator had scarcely rolled off the production line before work was started to convert the largest shop at the plant for the manufacture of portable power plants for these searchlights. Comparatively little new machinery was required. Presses that had been used for shaping refrigerator cabinets were utilized to make enclosures for the power units. The same spray-painting equipment was used. Parts for the power plants went through the same baking ovens that had been used for the refrigerators. The same conveyers carried the parts along the same assembly lines. Only 24 days elapsed before the first of the power units came off the production line.

Though they lacked some of the advantages of radar for antiaircraft fire direction, the big 60-inch searchlights served effectively against both Germany and Japan, particularly during the period when the SCR-584 radar set was in process of development. One of them employed during the campaign to recapture the Philippines is credited with having been instrumental in bringing down seven Jap planes.

In the United States large numbers of searchlights were stationed in areas subject to possible air-raid attack. Here they served a double purpose. They provided a means by which manually controlled antiaircraft guns could function at night, thereby permitting most of the radar fire-control equipment to be sent overseas. They served also to create the impression that the Army relied chiefly upon searchlights at night, while it was steadily placing greater reliance on radar.

"SMOOTHER" FOR TARGET TRACKING

Visual aiming of antiaircraft gun directors involved "tracking" the target in both elevation and azimuth. This was done by two men working with separate telescopes and hand cranks. Since it is almost impossible for anyone to crank a handwheel at a uniform speed throughout the rotation of the wheel, this method produces a jerky movement of the gun. Sometimes the gun points a little ahead of the target, and sometimes a little behind it. Thus a "smoother" is needed to eliminate the irregularities of hand cranking.

An effective device for this purpose was perfected and manufactured by the G.E. X-ray Corporation for 90-millimeter and 105-millimeter guns. Operation of the crank drove a small electric generator. The output of this generator went to a motor which transmitted the aiming information to the gun. In the circuit between the generator and the motor,

Floating power plant "Seapower" fitted with special bow section for trip across the Atlantic. After crossing she furnished power at Rotterdam.

Turbine-generator set of 30,000-kilowatt capacity installed in floating power plant.

Ship-to-shore power—complete substation mounted on deck of destroyer escort to supply electric power to land installations.

Boiler car of Navy 10,000-kilowatt power train with stack raised.

One of two 6-car power trains built for the Navy hooked up to supply emergency power for the Mare Island Navy Yard.

Cab of 600-kilowatt mobile, diesel-electric power unit for the U.S. Navy.

Trailer for transportation of Navy's 600-kilowatt diesel-electric power plant.

Large, fixed-location, radar station near sea coast. Shelters to house equipment are carefully camouflaged.

Cut-away sketch showing distribution of equipment at large, fixed-location radar stations.

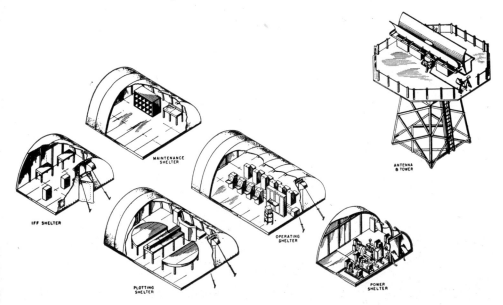

SCR-527 *required seven motor trucks for transportation.*

*Transmitter
trailer of the
SCR-527 radar
unit set up for
operation.*

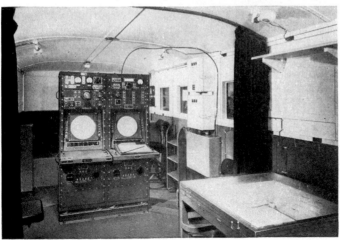

*Interior of operating
trailer of SCR-527 set*

Masts become more important than ever. Aloft on the U.S.S. Juneau are a variety of types of air and sea search radar antennas and radar jammers.

SP radar atop the main-mast for air and surface search.

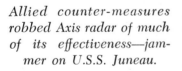

Allied counter-measures robbed Axis radar of much of its effectiveness—jammer on U.S.S. Juneau.

however, was a series of condensers that averaged out the
energy from the condenser and kept the motor at an average
speed.

This device had already been worked out in preliminary
form but the company ironed out the difficulties and developed it for production. Tests made by the Army firing at a
sleeve target towed by a moving plane showed that the
number of hits was increased 400 per cent through its use.

Effectiveness of gunfire in aerial warfare was materially
increased by improvements made by the Lamp Department
in gunsight lamps of a special reflector type. This type of
illumination was extremely important to ensure the visibility
of the gun sight when aiming against a bright background
such as a sunlit cloud, desert sand, or haze close to the sun.
Coupled with this improvement was the development of a
new device—a recording microphotometer—by which it was
possible to evaluate accurately the performance of experimental lamp designs.

A MISS AS GOOD AS A HIT

"That one's high, that one's low, where the hell did that
one go?" says the song of the field artillery. Shots that miss
the target, even though they may be fairly close to it, have
always been a headache to the artilleryman. Long before
the United States entered the war, both the Army and the
Navy were working on schemes to cause a projectile to explode when it reached the vicinity of its target without depending on a direct hit to detonate the charge. This was one
of the problems put up to the National Defense Research
Committee soon after its organization.

A device similar to radar provided the answer. It was the
VT or proximity fuse. This was a self-powered radio transmitter and receiver with miniature vacuum tubes and other
electronic components, small enough to fit into the base of an
antiaircraft shell and tough enough to withstand rough han-

dling. This set broadcast a continuous wave. When part of the wave was reflected back by striking an object, it interacted with the outgoing wave, and the shell then exploded at an ideal distance to give maximum effect to the flying pieces and fragments.

Demand for large-volume manufacture of the vital little glass tubes was immediate after the development of the new type fuse. Their manufacture was proceeding slowly, however, until the problem was put up to lamp-bulb engineers at Nela Park, Cleveland. They saw at once the similarity between the production problem and that of the ordinary, small Christmas-tree lamp.

Since the tiny tube had to be made with watchlike precision, and since it was slightly different in shape from the Christmas-tree lamp, some adjustments were required in the production machinery. They were quickly made. When manufacture started, the tubes were turned out by the millions at Christmas-tree lamp prices—about one-eighth of what the government had been previously paying for the same thing.

Manufacture of the proximity fuse at Bridgeport and Schenectady was shrouded in secrecy. Thousands of workers were employed on the project, but none of them knew what it was, or the intended purpose of the particular part he was making. Heavily armed guards accompanied all shipments of the fuse.

In battle the proximity fuse was at first employed only in areas where duds could not land in enemy territory and the secrets of their design be discovered. Later, it was more widely used. Against the Japanese Kamikaze bombers and against the German buzz bombs, it proved highly effective. In the Battle of the Bulge it gave excellent results. At Iwo Jima and Okinawa it was used during the attack to disrupt enemy gun operation, and also for defense against enemy aircraft. Altogether, its development was a powerful addition to the arsenal of the United Nations.

ELECTRIC GUN DIRECTION ON SHIPS

Naval guns are used principally against moving targets— enemy surface ships and enemy aircraft. The latter, especially, move at high speeds. Moreover, the ship from which the gun is fired is, itself, moving, rolling, and pitching. For these reasons the problems of correctly aiming a naval gun are quite different from those of aiming a gun on land.

Even before World War I the United States Navy employed elaborate fire-control systems on its ships to aim the guns so that shells and target would arrive at the same point at the same time. In the 1920's, however, electricity came to play a major part in naval fire control. Early types of equipment for this purpose were designed and built by the Navy itself. But the Navy's facilities were limited and it was not long before General Electric was brought into the picture, first as a consultant and later as a producer. The company was, in fact, the first commercial manufacturer to build electric fire-control apparatus for the Navy.

The gunfire-control system used on American warships in World War II had four principal parts: a director, a stable element, a computer, and the guns themselves. The director was the eye of the system. Located high up on the structure of the ship where it had an unobstructed view, it was the means of determining the direction and distance to the target. This could be done either by radar or by telescopes and an optical range finder. After the direction and distance had been determined, the information was sent below decks to the computer. The stable element, located in the plotting room deep down inside the ship, was a gyroscopic device that sent information to the computer on the roll and pitch of the vessel.

The computer, located in the plotting room, was the brains of the system. From the data it received from the director and the stable element, as well as other data on the course and speed of its own ship, wind, etc., it automatically determined where the guns should be pointed so that the shells and the target would arrive simultaneously at the same place. This information was then sent to the guns, which were the fists of the system. They were aimed by hydraulic or electric power drives, usually automatically, in accordance with the information received from the computer. They were fired automatically at a predetermined instant, or manually on orders from the gunnery officer.

Electricity was the life blood of these fire-control systems. The importance and complexity of its work is illustrated by the fact that the Mark 34 gun director of 6-inch and 8-inch guns had a total of 345 electric wires connecting with other elements in the fire-control system. The wiring of the director itself was so complex that engineers estimated that there were more than 11,000 different mistakes that could be made in connecting the wires. General Electric built these and other directors for all kinds of Navy ships. On cruisers, they controlled the main batteries, 8-inch guns, and 6-inch guns, and on battleships, aircraft carriers, cruisers, and destroyers they controlled the 5-inch guns.

Once, after a strenuous night battle between American and Japanese naval vessels in the Western Pacific, a United States destroyer fished out of the water a half-drowned Jap officer—one of the few survivors of his sunken ship. Hardly had he reached the destroyer's deck when he asked eagerly to see "your 5-inch machine gun with the electric-eye pointer." He was referring to the destroyer's main batteries, operated so fast and accurately that he thought they were huge machine guns.

The company also built the stable elements for battleships and hydraulic controls for the big 16-inch guns of the main batteries. Hydraulic control was developed for the Navy's dual-purpose 5-inch guns. Its reliability and accuracy were so outstanding that the company was required to produce these units in large numbers, even though it was necessary to construct and equip a huge new building for their manufacture. Thousands of amplidyne power drives were made for 1.1-inch and 40-millimeter antiaircraft guns—equipment so designed that the guns could follow a fast-moving attacking plane with great accuracy regardless of the roll of the sea.

OPTICAL RIFLE-SIGHTING GAUGE

Correct aim is just as necessary to hit the target with a small rifle as it is with a big 16-inch gun. But the soldier firing a small rifle has no radar and gun director. He must depend on his own eyes and on the sights on the barrel of the rifle.

Formerly, when army rifles were manufactured at a rate of a few thousand a year, the sights were adjusted at the Springfield Arsenal by actual firing of the rifle. This process involved the firing of about a dozen shots per rifle. It took two men about 5 minutes to make the necessary adjustments. When the government was faced with the problem of producing rifles by the millions for World War II, the old method of sight testing was too slow. Something faster and better was urgently needed.

To meet this situation, General Electric's General Engineering Laboratory developed a new device, a special optical sighting gauge. What this apparatus did, essentially, was to transfer the sight setting from a "master" rifle, correctly sighted by actual firing, to new rifles coming off the production line. This was done by placing the new rifle in a rack and inserting a plug in the muzzle with its axis coinciding with the axis of the bore. The plug carried a concave mirror, from which a beam of light was reflected back to another mirror and thence to a near-by screen. When the image coincided with the prescribed marking on the screen, the rifle was in position for sighting. The rear sight was then adjusted until its shadow, magnified twenty-five times on the screen of a projector immediately above it, was in the same relative position as the shadow of the front sight, similarly magnified in another projector.

This gauge saved the ammunition formerly used in sighting the gun, and permitted a girl to do the job in less than 2 minutes. Moreover, the equipment occupied only a small room, whereas sighting by firing required a 100-yard rifle range.

Soldiers on the firing line knew only that the sights on their rifles were accurately set. They never heard of this sight gauge. But it was a highly effective means of providing them with accurate weapons.

14

Radio for Combat Communication

WHILE THE ART OF "radio detection and ranging" was being developed and perfected, notable progress was being made also in the art of radio communication. Accomplishments in this field were, indeed, responsible for far reaching changes in the tactical concepts of warfare in World War II.

SCOUTING IN THE SOUTH PACIFIC

A typical example was seen one day in the South Pacific. High on a hilltop overlooking the wide expanse of tropical landscape sat a brown-skinned native. His keen eyes followed every movement of the yellow-skinned soldiers in the valley below. From time to time he spoke briefly into the mouthpiece of a portable radio. Miles away a group of officers of the United States Marines sat talking in the shade of a weather-beaten tent. One of them was wearing a pair of headphones. From time to time he interrupted the conversation to relay the news he was receiving from the native on the hilltop.

Outside the tent hundreds of Marines were in a bustle of activity. Final preparations were being made for an amphibious landing to be made at dawn the next morning. Its success might depend on accurate knowledge of the numbers and positions of the enemy on the shore where the landing would be made. An English-speaking native, previously taught how to operate a portable radio set, had been landed in the dark from a PT boat on an unoccupied beach. Gaining a hilltop which overlooked the Japanese positions, he was now describing the situation in detail to the distant officers of the Marine landing force. To the old art of scouting had been added instant, on-the-spot reporting.

That kind of scouting was a characteristic of World War II. Whether the scout did his work afoot, in a tank, jeep, plane, or boat, he almost always did it with a radio to communicate with headquarters.

PROGRESS IN MILITARY COMMUNICATIONS

Such speed in transmitting intelligence represented a revolutionary change in warfare from the early days of visual signals and couriers on foot or on horseback. Napoleon introduced a new feature by setting up large fixed semaphores along the seacoast to warn of enemy fleet movements, and telescopes were employed to read their signals from considerable distances. The telegraph was first used during the American Civil War. In World War I was seen the first employment of radio in a major conflict. The equipment, however, consisted mainly of spark sets of limited usefulness. Only toward the end of the war did the transition from spark to tube sets begin.

Following that conflict, the many changes in military methods demanded changes in means of communication. Most significant was the vastly increased use of aircraft; next came the widespread employment of automotive vehicles such as tanks, half-tracks, self-propelled guns, scout cars, and various other wheeled and amphibious vehicles. All of them—planes and vehicles—had to be able to communicate with each other and with the various headquarters in the chain of command.

New methods of communication were devised, since wire communication would not suffice. Radio became essential to assure unity of action among the fast-moving and diverse elements of the fighting forces. New types of radio equipment were designed for tanks, scout cars, and planes, and for field communication between infantry units; and extra lightweight sets were placed on the backs of infantry and air-borne troops.

Need for these instruments had been foreseen. In the years preceding the outbreak of World War II, Army and Navy authorities in the United States had recognized the necessity for new types of combat communication equipment, and in 1934 Congress appropriated limited funds for development work. These funds were later increased under the National Defense program.

Technical problems involved in the design of the new equipment were extraordinarily difficult. The apparatus had to be light in weight, occupy a minimum of space, and be of exceptionally sturdy construction to permit placement in combat vehicles operating over all kinds of terrain. Design problems were equally difficult for air-borne and shipboard radio. To complicate the problem further, it was necessary that many types of equipment be arranged for voice instead of operation with a telegraph key and sounder or both.

There were several reasons for this. One was greater speed. A man can talk a good deal faster than he can pound a telegraph key. Even more important was simplicity of operation. Members of the crews of tanks and planes have a multiplicity of jobs to perform. Communications must be maintained without interruption to the performance of other duties. A gunner in a tank can talk and keep on working his gun. An airplane pilot can talk while he continues to maneuver his plane.

Virtually every bomber flown by the Army Air Forces carried a 75-watt radio set known as the "SCR-287" with long-range transmitter for both voice and key operation. This transmitter was a new development undertaken some years before the outbreak of the war and was already in production at General Electric's Schenectady Works at the time of Pearl Harbor. Approximately 70,000 were produced during the course of the war.

At the same time some 40,000 transmitters of a somewhat similar type were produced for the Army Ground Forces. These versatile, sturdy transmitters were of inestimable value in establishing the hundreds of tactical and administrative radio networks required by the army.

RADIO ON VEHICLES

In the 1930's the SCR-193 was the Army's most extensively used, medium-range radio set. It was mounted in almost every type of vehicle operated by the armed forces. Its design was rather old-fashioned, however, and one of the first development tasks undertaken was to bring it up to date.

The SCR-193 was used for telegraph communication only, and at first the idea was to employ the new set for the same purpose. The General Electric Company, which had for some years been making the transmitters for the SCR-193, was asked to undertake the design of the new set, which was to be called the "SCR-506."

Its design had been almost completed when the Army Air Forces demanded that the new set should carry voice communication. Under battle conditions, they pointed out, close liaison had to be maintained between the vehicles on the ground and planes aloft. They had to have voice equipment because their fliers simply could not handle dot-and-dash messages in addition to their other duties.

This new requirement was a backbreaker. Tubes, switches, coils, and other equipment had already been crowded together into the smallest possible framework. Where could the additional equipment for voice operation be put? There was nothing to do but rearrange the interior so that a few more components could be squeezed in.

Somehow the job was done. Experimental models of the new set were completed late in 1941 and submitted for approval. Then began a series of trials to determine how the set worked under field conditions.

PUNISHMENT TESTS AT FORT RILEY

The equipment was subjected to the most rigid punishment tests known to the Army. At noontime one day on the hot, dusty plains near Fort Riley an Army command car was banging along over the rough ground. A cavalry officer and a soldier driver occupied the front seat. In the rear was a civilian engineer operating a SCR-506 radio set. Everyone was tired, hungry, and disgusted. The whole morning had been spent bouncing over bumps in an endeavor to jolt the radio out of business. But they had failed. The set had taken the bumps and was still going strong as ever.

It was time to eat and the crew were becoming impatient. "Gimme the wheel," exclaimed the officer, "and I'll finish off that damn set."

He grabbed the wheel and stepped on the gas. The command car went lurching wildly over the uneven ground and then raced madly down a hill. Suddenly a deep ditch loomed ahead. The cavalry officer, forgetting, perhaps, that he was riding a piece of automotive equipment and not a piece of horseflesh, decided to jump it. The front wheels reached the far side of the ditch but the rear wheels failed to make it. With a crash the car came to a stop, half in and half out of the gulley. The civilian engineer had jumped, but the officer and the radio operator had not had time and were badly shaken up. As they crawled out of the wrecked car the officer growled grimly. "That's fixed the radio, anyway!"

To make sure, they tried it. To everyone's surprise it spoke up loud and clear. They had smashed the car, but they hadn't succeeded in smashing the radio. So they used it to call Fort Riley and get help to pull the car out of the ditch. That night the set was used successfully in communication with Fort Monmouth, more than 1,600 miles away.

This was but one of the many punishment tests given to the SCR-506. It was sent out on trips through rain and mud, and through sun, heat, and dust. No weather was too bad, no road was too rough. Out of these severe tests came indisputable evidence that the SCR-506 was a real toughie—powerful and reliable, and sturdy enough for operation under the most grueling conditions.

In 1942, thousands of these sets began to roll off the G-E production line. Originally designed for operation in command tanks, it provided instant selection of any one of four pretuned frequencies and of one variable frequency. With this arrangement it could communicate with equal ease with other tanks, infantry, command posts, airplanes, and headquarters back some distance from the front. It was also possible to make quick shifts from one frequency to another in the middle of a message and thus prevent more than a part being overheard by the enemy. This versatility, plus its compactness and sturdiness, led to its adoption for general use in other vehicles besides tanks—in half-tracks, armored cars, scout cars, trucks, amphibious vehicles, and even the ubiquitous jeep.

Radio was here, there, and everywhere with the Army. It landed on the Normandy beaches. It rumbled through France with the fast-moving American columns. It controlled traffic on the roads behind the front. It summoned the help that pinched off the big German bulge in the Ardennes. And when the Rhine was reached, radio continued to play a vital role in breaking that formidable barrier.

RADIO FOR THE NAVY

The company had also been active before the war in radio development for the Navy. There the communication needs were radically different from those of the Army. Distances to be covered were generally far greater. Messages were transmitted and received by specially trained operators who had no other duties to perform. A large ship could easily carry a number of different radio sets for different purposes. Speed was important, of course, but it was not necessary to have the almost instantaneous speed of voice communication. Under these circumstances it was the Navy's feeling that the greater range and accuracy of radio telegraph made it preferable to radio telephone for most purposes. Then, too, the telegraph permitted secret messages to be transmitted in code with smaller opportunity for the enemy to intercept and translate them for his own information.

Radio communication by spark sets was extensively used by the U.S. Navy in World War I. Numerous advances and improvements in design were made in following years. Many of them were worked out for the Navy by General Electric. Every type of transmitter above 24 kilowatts, in fact, was produced by the company. Among them were the three great 500,000-watt units for shore stations capable of reaching any part of the world. So efficient was their design that they were able to operate days on end without interruption. Altogether the company was supplying a substantial part of the radio equipment for the Navy during this period.

By the time World War II broke out, the Navy had more or less standardized its radio communications. One innovation, however, was a G-E portable transmitting and receiving set known as the "TBX" for the Marine Corps. This was light in weight and convenient for use in amphibious operations. It was so sturdy that it could be tossed overboard from a ship and washed ashore by the waves without incurring any damage. It could be quickly set up by a landing party and used to report its position, indicate enemy gun locations, direct supporting artillery fire, and call for air coverage, reinforcements, or supplies. This set went in with the Marines at Guadalcanal, Bougainville, Saipan, and Okinawa and everywhere rendered invaluable service.

Except for the development of the TBX, the wartime changes in Navy radio were largely improvements in components rather than redesign or new design of complete sets. The volume of equipment demands, however, increased enormously. The Navy was operating a far larger number of ships than ever before in its whole history, and was using many more radio sets per ship. Previously a fairly large ship might have had three or four radio sets; now it had twenty or thirty. The limiting factor, indeed, seemed to be only the number of antennas for which room could be found. Under the impetus of this demand, the production of the company's Radio Department soared to heights many times higher than ever before.

WIRE RECORDER

Closely associated with radio was General Electric's production of the wire recorder, used in great numbers by both the Army and the Navy. By this means 66 minutes of continuous speech could be recorded magnetically on 15,000 feet of hairlike steel wire on a small spool. Instead of making notes with a pad and pencil, a military or naval observer had only to dictate into a small microphone like a business executive using a dictaphone. After the recording had been completed in the battle area, the spool could be sent to headquarters for playback of the information or sent to a radio station and the whole report transmitted back to any location where a full, word-by-word description of the proceedings was desired. Some of these recordings were used for press work and several were put on national radio chains shortly after they were made. When there was no further use for the talk the recording could be "wiped off" magnetically and the wire used for future recordings. On the other hand, the report could be allowed to remain and be repeated as many times as desired.

TRANSOCEANIC BROADCASTS

After Marconi's first demonstration that messages could be transmitted without wires, the effective use of radio was limited for many years by the relatively weak power of the spark and arc transmitters. What was needed was a practical generator to produce more powerful signals. This problem was tackled with vigor and determination by a young General Electric engineer named E. F. W. Alexanderson. Progress was slow, but step by step he went ahead until eventually he had completed the design of a powerful generator that metamorphosed radio. His 200-kilowatt machine, installed in 1918 in the big station of the American Marconi Company at New Brunswick, N.J., became the foundation of the first great transoceanic radio system.

From that time onward the company's activity in long-range radio transmission never slackened. It not only built powerful equipment for both commercial and military use, but also built and operated for experimental purposes its own short-wave broadcasting stations. In the 1930's two of these stations, WGEA and WGEO located near Schenectady, were sending out regular programs beamed to South America and Europe.

To this pair of stations a third was added in 1939. A new short-wave transmitter with special antenna was one of the company's exhibits at the Golden Gate International Exposition at San Francisco and it was decided to broadcast news and music every day to Asia and South America. This transmitter was known as Station "KGEI." The experiment was rather a shot in the dark, but it hit the bull's-eye.

Cablegrams and letters poured in from hundreds of homesick Americans in China, Burma, Japan, and the South Pacific islands.

"At last we can tune in on some real unbiased news," they said.

After Pearl Harbor the transoceanic broadcasts by General Electric's short-wave stations became a potent weapon in the hands of the United Nations. In the dark days when the Axis powers were advancing everywhere, the people in the occupied countries of Europe and the Pacific might have lost their last vestige of hope if radio had not sent them words of encouragement.

To thousands of Frenchmen, Poles, Danes, Finns, Czechs, Greeks, and others, the voices of WGEO and WGEA spoke daily in their native language, telling them the truth in the face of Axis misstatements, and bringing them messages of fresh hope and renewed confidence. Regular programs were broadcast in eleven languages. A steady trickle of fan mail came back to Schenectady from listeners all over the world, many of whom tuned in at the risk of their lives, and whose letters were smuggled out of occupied territory with the greatest of difficulty.

A Frenchwoman, driven by the Germans from her home in Lorraine, wrote to the WGEA French announcer:

Abandoned almost by everyone here, the certainty of deliverance which you gave us enables us to endure this long exile as well as the privations of every kind. England and the great American nation will be victorious and once more will save us.

May you be blessed, American people, and may the ever-victorious Star-Spangled Banner soon float under our French sky. In the hope of seeing our army beside you, associated with those who have heroically saved the honor of France, please accept, Mr. Announcer, our profound gratitude.

Portable radar set—receiver and transmitter are inside the tent, antenna on mast.

Set up and ready for operation —transmitter and receiver of small portable radar.

Airborne radar equipment in unpressurized section of B-29 bomber.

Principal elements of light-weight, airborne radar—antenna at left; radar scope atop control box; transmitter and receiver.

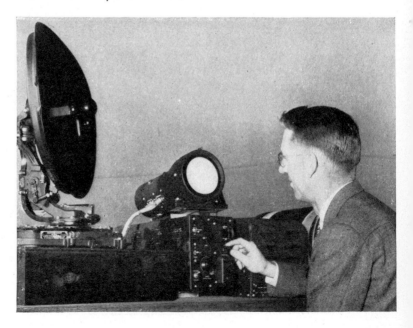

Searchlight and sound locator—widely used for aircraft detection in the early days of the war.

Checking completed 60-inch antiaircraft searchlights at Erie.

Beam of the 800,000,000-candlepower, 60-inch searchlight was so bright that a newspaper could be read at a distance of eight miles.

G-E portable power plants for antiaircraft searchlights in test section at Erie Works.

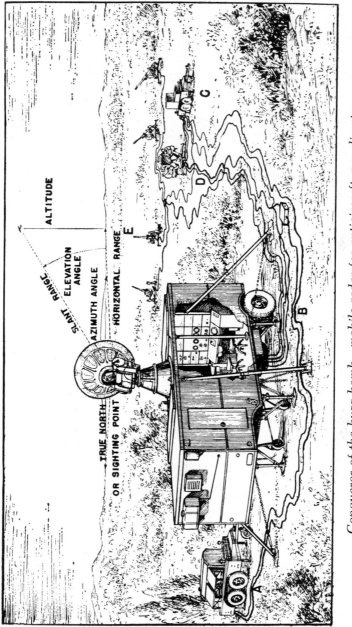

Conqueror of the buzz bomb—mobile radar for antiaircraft gun directors.

To make gunfire more effective—gun director mounted on fire control tower aboard a U.S. Warship.

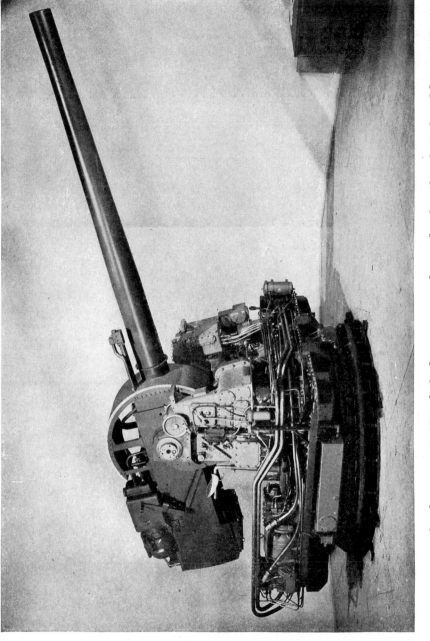

Hydraulic mount for 5-inch dual-purpose naval gun, developed and produced by General Electric.

Dual purpose 5-inch guns aboard the U.S.S. Fletcher provided with G-E hydraulic control.

Optical rifle sighting gage saved ammunition and time in adjusting sights on new rifles.

*Radio on wheels—U.S. Army's versatile "506" radio com-
munication set mounted in a jeep.*

*Radio set "506" removed from its jeep
and ready for operation in a "dugout" in
the Southwest Pacific.*

Portable radio in operation on Guadalcanal.

Making radio transmitters for U.S. Navy at Schenectady. Every type of Navy transmitter above 24 kilowatts was produced by the company.

First hand battle reports—U.S. Marines relate their Bougainville experiences to magnetic wire recorder made by General Electric.

Description of German U-boat surrender off Cape May, N.J., being put on wire recorder.

Voice of encouragement to occupied countries—antenna of inter-national short-wave radio broadcasting station WGEA.

X-ray chest examination of men inducted into Armed Forces. Twelve million such examinations were made.

Million-volt x-ray machine for treatment of deep seated malignancy at Walter Reed General Hospital.

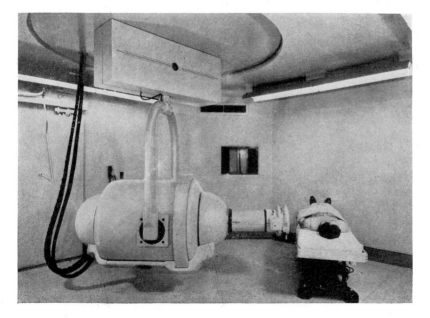

Dental X-ray examination aboard hospital ship
U.S.S. Repose.

X-ray equipment was shipped in record-breaking
quantities to the Armed Forces.

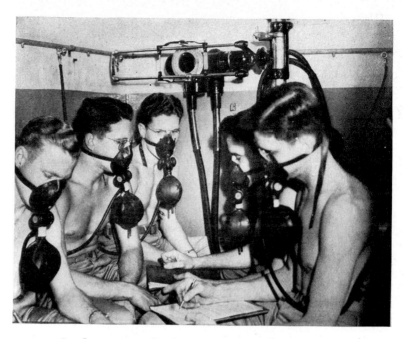

Students at Medical School of Northwestern University undergoing X-ray tests in altitude chamber.

World's fastest merry-go-round, used to test airplane pilot's resistance to effects of centrifugal force.

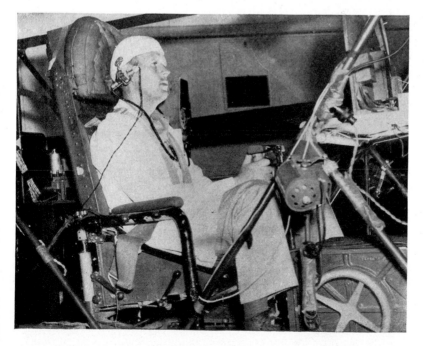

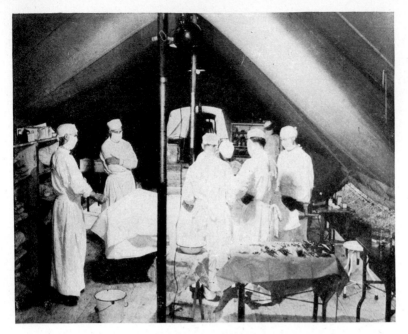

Special electric spotlight aids emergency operation in Army field hospital.

Wounded soldiers receiving blood-plasma transfusions on Normandy beachhead. Refrigeration was vital in transportation of blood-plasma.

From the opposite side of the continent Station KGEI at San Francisco and a second station known as "KGEX" were directing a similar radio barrage at Asia and the islands of the Pacific. As part of their plan for the Greater East Asia Co-Prosperity Sphere, the Japanese had flooded China, Indo-China, Burma, Malaya, and the Philippines with hundreds of thousands of cheap short-wave receivers so that the natives would listen to Radio Tokyo. But they figured without Station KGEI. In many of these lands the American programs came booming in far louder than those of the Japs, lifting the spirits of both the conquered peoples and of the United Nations' forces endeavoring to liberate them.

As the flag of the Rising Sun at first swept onward in the Southwest Pacific, the spirits of the small group of Americans in Japanese-controlled Shanghai dropped lower and lower. Few people knew what was actually happening. The newspapers published only the propaganda of the Japs. Victory after victory for the sons of Nippon was reported.

In the dark of the late evening a stealthy American slipped quietly into a small building just off the Bubbling Well Road. Then another, and another and presently half a dozen were gathered in a stuffy attic room. All lights were out. Not a sound was to be heard. Suddenly the silence was broken by a calm, pleasant voice.

Station KGEI is on the air!
The Navy Department reports an engagement off the island of Midway. Task forces under the command of Adms. Frank J. Fletcher and Raymond A. Spruance sighted a large enemy fleet apparently heading for Hawaii.

And the voice continued with an account of the battle.

The furtive Americans listened intently as the voice from San Francisco told how torpedo bombers from the U.S.S. *Hornet* scored hits on four Japanese carriers; how others from the U.S.S. *Yorktown* and *Enterprise* took up the attack and hit two more Jap flattops, a battleship, and a cruiser; how dive bombers and submarines raced in and finished the job; how the enemy turned tail and started to run, losing four more cruisers and a destroyer before the battle was broken off—the worst defeat the Japanese had suffered since the Korean admiral Yi-Sun had smashed the Nipponese fleet off the coast of Korea in 1592.

The listening Americans clasped hands and smiled. A husky voice murmured, "Thank God for KGEI."

15

Health and Medicine

ELECTRICITY SERVED THE ARMED FORCES effectively not only in combat but also in the fight to preserve health and save human lives. X ray, electromedical equipment, air conditioning, and refrigeration were the heavy artillery in this struggle.

HOW X-RAY DISCOVERED UNEXPLODED SHELL

On an island in the Pacific portable X-ray equipment in an emergency hospital played the leading part in one of the most dramatic feats of surgery recorded during the war. A young sailor, while standing at his post on the deck of a U.S. destroyer, was hit by a 20-millimeter shell during a battle off the Solomon Islands. It struck him just below his left chest, pierced his intestines, and lodged in his left hip. It did not explode, but remained lodged in the flesh of his leg. On a near-by battleship an emergency operation was performed on his intestinal tract, and he remained in the battleship's sick bay while the fight continued. At its conclusion he was moved to an emergency naval hospital on a neighboring island. There a hunt began for the unexploded shell.

Two Navy surgeons, working behind a steel plate, made X-ray pictures until the shell was definitely located. Once the exact position was determined, the deft fingers of the surgeons had it out in a few minutes. The shell was then turned over to Marine Ordnance and exploded. Commenting on this episode in a letter addressed to the men and women of the General Electric X-ray Corporation, Rear Admiral W. B. Young told them, "You may be proud of producing such essential equipment for the Navy."

12 MILLION EXAMINATIONS AT INDUCTION CENTERS

During World War I, an X-ray chest examination was not a routine procedure for men inducted into the armed forces. As a result, the government later had to pay out more than a billion dollars in claims and hospitalization on tuberculosis cases which showed up while the men were in service.

When the United States entered World War II, General Electric X-ray units were installed in selective service induction centers throughout the country to examine the chests of all draftees to prevent men with tuberculosis from making their way into the ranks. Since these units produced an X-ray image of the chest on a 4- by 5-inch film, instead of the conventional 14- by 17-inch film, material costs were cut to about one-tenth of those of the older method.

During the war years after Congress passed the Selective Service Act, about 12 million X-ray examinations were made at induction stations. They resulted in 120,000 deferments for chest conditions, though most of the men concerned had no idea that these conditions existed. In one instance, it was found that two men out of three who were rejected because of tuberculosis were not aware that they had the disease.

Dental and medical diagnostic and therapeutic X-rays installed at army field hospitals and aboard hospital ships were invaluable in locating the sources of numerous body disorders and in treating some of them. Powerful yet portable X-ray equipment found use where troops were constantly on the move. Special units offered a combination of fluoroscopy, diagnosis, and therapy, all in one apparatus.

For therapeutic purposes, special high-voltage units were developed, ranging from 200,000 to 1,000,000 volts. At the Army Medical Center, Walter Reed General Hospital, an extremely compact million-volt therapy unit was installed. This apparatus could be used with little skin damage, since it concentrated a high dosage deep within the tissues. It could be used with slight danger of severe changes in the blood and less intense radiation sickness, thus permitting the administration of larger amounts of radiation.

Electromedical equipment produced by the company found application in numerous military installations. The Army alone purchased hundreds of electrocardiographs, by which the tiny electrical potential created by the action of the heart is magnified electronically and recorded photographically on film. Ultraviolet lamps found widespread use in treating a variety of ills. Also in considerable demand were inductotherms to generate the high-frequency current that induces heat deep within the tissues without contact. A special type of inductotherm was developed with crystal control so that its frequency could be precisely regulated to avoid interference with near-by radio apparatus.

X RAY ABOARD THE U.S.S. *FRANKLIN*

Service of inestimable value was rendered by the X-ray equipment aboard the U.S.S. *Franklin* when the big aircraft carrier was nearly destroyed by fire and explosions caused by enemy bombs off the coast of Japan. The heroic efforts of the crew, many of them continuing, despite their injuries, to fight the raging flames for hours, not only kept the ship afloat, but eventually brought her home, 12,000 miles away under her own power. In the midst of the turmoil and the struggle to save the ship, X ray was doing wonders in determining the extent of injuries to members of her crew and as a diagnostic aid in the treatment of those who had been wounded.

In a telegram to the men and women of General Electric X-ray Corporation, Vice-Admiral Ross T. McIntire, Chief of the Bureau of Medicine and Surgery, said,

The splendid performance of an X-ray machine of your manufacture aboard the U.S.S *Franklin* is cited in a report of the medical officer of this carrier. . . . In behalf of the men of the *Franklin* and of the countless other Navy men who have benefited from your equipment, the Bureau extends sincere thanks.

TESTS FOR HIGH-ALTITUDE FLIERS

Research was carried on by means of X ray during the war to determine what happens to the organs of the human body at high altitudes. Tests were made in a special decompression chamber at the Medical School of Northwestern University, where conditions were reproduced similar to those encountered when flying at an elevation of 38,000 feet or more than 7 miles up.

Danger often arises at high altitudes from the expansion of gases within the body as outside pressure is reduced. Particles of gases that lodge in fat tissue and joints expand and cause severe pain to the fliers. A group of students at the university volunteered to act as "aviators" for the purpose of the test. They were provided with oxygen masks and seated in the decompression chamber, which was equipped with shockproof X-ray apparatus mounted on an adjustable stand.

X-ray pictures were taken from time to time of the heart, lungs, joints, and muscles of the "aviators." These showed significant changes with variations in pressure and provided flight surgeons and research men with important new information in their battle against the dangers of high-altitude flying, particularly the "bends."

WORLD'S FASTEST MERRY-GO-ROUND

Other tests for fliers were made on the world's fastest merry-go-round—one that swung a man like a pail of water at the end of a rope. This was the human "centrifuge" developed by the Army Air Forces and used at the Aero-Medical Laboratory at Wright Field, Ohio. Its purpose was to study how much strain above or below the normal force of gravity a pilot could take without losing consciousness.

The centrifuge machine, for which General Electric built the powerful electric drive and also the delicate control mechanism, consisted of a horizontal boom with a driving shaft at its center. Cockpits were mounted near each end of the boom, 20 feet from the center shaft. The boom turned as rapidly as 54 revolutions per minute, and could reach this speed in 5 seconds from standstill. It could be stopped in the same time, thus simulating the most severe operating conditions to be encountered in flying an airplane.

While whirling the subject at high speed, the machine tilted him in such a position that he was affected as though he were pulling out of a steep dive at a speed of 500 miles an hour. Delicate instruments attached to him recorded his blood pressure, pulse, and respiration, and the speed of his reactions was tested by the time he took to return signals flashed to him by an observer.

With this machine the physical limitations of a human pilot could be determined with great accuracy. This information was then utilized by the airplane designers to make sure that the speed and maneuverability of new planes would not exceed the limits of what the fliers could stand—an assurance that was of inestimable value in combat with the enemy.

AIR CONDITIONING, AN AID TO MEDICINE

Nearly every Army camp, Naval base, and hospital in the country used refrigeration equipment supplied by the company. It was employed for air-conditioning operating rooms, cooling, and refrigeration storage rooms for biologicals, in processing rooms where blood plasma was desiccated, in food-storage rooms, in photographic and X-ray film developing rooms, in oxygen tents, water and beverage coolers, and elsewhere.

The role of air conditioning in the field of medicine was already great when the war broke out, but with the discovery and use of new drugs like penicillin, its importance rose. To remove water from penicillin mold required boiling and evaporation, but boiling at normal temperatures would have damaged the life-giving mold. Hence, refrigeration-pumping equipment came into the picture, lowering the pressure in the mold chambers, until the water could be boiled off at an extremely low temperature. Careful temperature control was important too. During the early stages of the drug's manufacture, the cultures must be heated and cooled at just the proper intervals, and refrigeration helped accomplish this job—making larger and larger quantities of penicillin available to the armed forces.

REFRIGERATED CONTAINERS FOR BLOOD

Shortly before the war a refrigerated container service was started for the transportation by rail of small shipments of perishable commodities such as fish, meat, poultry, vegetables, cheese, ice cream, and serum and vaccines. The fact that small shipments could move in this way opened up new markets for refrigerated products.

These containers, built at the Erie Works, looked like large trunks made of galvanized steel and mounted on casters so they could be moved easily; the interior capacity was 10 cubic feet. A bunker which could be loaded with 100 pounds of dry ice or 90 pounds of water ice provided the low temperature required, and 4 inches of insulation around the outside of the container assured the maintenance of this low temperature.

With the advent of the war the Red Cross was faced with the problem of shipping blood from its many collection centers to the eight laboratories where processing was done. These shipments had to reach the laboratories within 24 hours and be maintained during transit at a uniform temperature close to 40 degrees Fahrenheit or the blood would become useless, a requirement that threatened to bog down the whole project.

The improved procedure was to take the blood from the arm of the donor and put it in a pint bottle, which was then placed in an unbleached muslin bag and stored in a refrigerator at a temperature between 35 and 40 degrees. Meanwhile, a traveling container was being precooled to a temperature of 20 degrees below zero. At a fixed time each evening the bottles were transferred to the refrigerated container, 80 pints to a box, and a truck came to take the container to the railroad station for loading on a fast train. At the end of the trip another truck delivered the containers to a laboratory, where the liquid blood was transformed by centrifugal spinning, freezing, and dehydrating into a crystalline substance that could be preserved indefinitely.

The shipment of blood began in a small way, but as the number of blood donations increased, more and more containers, which had been moving commercial shipments, were pressed into service to handle them. Soon there were hardly enough available containers to meet this growing need, though the original number had been greatly augmented by that time. The government then ordered that all existing containers be used for blood exclusively. It later became imperative that still more containers be obtained. The War Production Board granted the necessary priorities, and the Erie Works took on the job of making them. Despite the great volume of other jobs then in progress, the plant turned out hundreds of additional containers to keep the transportation of blood flowing smoothly.

Colonel C. F. Snook of the Army Medical Corps said,

Upon my recent inspection of one of the processing laboratories for blood plasma, I noted the presence of the new containers. It was indeed with a sigh of relief that I noted this problem gradually being solved.

Your company has been more than cooperative and has assisted this office materially in the procurement and distribution of this commodity. The Surgeon General has directed that I express his appreciation of your endeavors.

16

Meeting Needs for More Power

PARALLELING ITS PRODUCTION of combat equipment for the armed forces, General Electric made a wide variety of products to expedite the work of industries engaged in the war effort. Generators, transformers, and switchgear provided and delivered essential electric power for industry. Motors drove the machine tools in war-production plants all over the country. Electric welding speeded the construction of ships and tanks and countless other products. Improved lighting promoted more efficient operation of war plants. New materials were developed to meet special needs. A wide variety of testing and measuring instruments and apparatus was produced. And for that most amazing achievement, the development of the atomic bomb, the company furnished huge amounts of equipment requiring the highest order of technical and engineering skill in design and production. These contributions for industry, no less than those directly for the armed forces, paved the road to ultimate victory.

America's job of providing equipment and supplies in World War II was about 3½ times as big as the job done in World War I. If the 1918 level of productive efficiency prevailed in 1941–45, more than 78 billion man-hours of labor per year would have been required. Even for the populous United States, this would have been an impossible assignment. There simply were not enough men and women available to perform that amount of work. Actually, the job was done with 32 billion man-hours of work—plus the most intensive utilization of electric power ever seen.

On Armistice Day, 1918, the United States had only 1¼ horsepower of electric-generating capacity available per worker. On V-J Day, 1945, it had more than 5 horsepower per worker. That was the key to success in America's great war production effort.

To accomplish its record-breaking volume of war production, American industry had to smash a number of bottlenecks. The first was a shortage of machine tools. Then came scarcity of essential metals—steel, aluminum, and magnesium. Later there were shortages of rubber and gasoline. But at no time was there any scarcity of electric power. When shipyards, aircraft plants, oil refineries, and munitions plants all called for more electric power at the same time, the demand was met.

It was something of a miracle that the electric-power industry had sufficient generating capacity to satisfy all war demands, but it was the sort of miracle in which foresight had a large part. Additions to generating capacity had been made steadily during the years following World War I, reaching a peak in 1930. Then came a slump. Little new equipment was bought during the next few years when general business activity was at a low level. Had this policy continued, the outbreak of World War II would have found the United States facing a serious shortage of electric power.

FORESIGHT IN PROVIDING INCREASED GENERATING CAPACITY

There were men, however, who foresaw that failure to continue expansion of generating facilities would inevitably lead to trouble later. Among them was M. O. Troy, manager of G.E.'s Central Station Department. Even while the electric power generating industry appeared to have more capacity than was needed, he organized a vigorous campaign to promote the installation of more capacity. He pointed out that there already existed enough electrically operated machinery and apparatus in the country to create an overwhelming demand for electric power if industrial activity increased sharply. He emphasized the length of time required to build a turbine-generator—a minimum of 12 months—and urged the power industry to start preparing for the future. To show the strength of its belief in its own argument, the company began to procure material and build ten turbines, though at the moment there were no buyers in sight for these machines.

The soundness of this policy became apparent before long. Power demands commenced to increase. By 1936 they had reached a point substantially higher than the previous peak. In 1938, President Roosevelt undertook a serious study of the adequacy of the electric-power supply for national defense. Under the impetus of these various factors and the threatening war clouds in Europe, the power industry became active in placing orders for generating equipment. All the ten generators which the company had built in anticipation of future needs were sold. In fact there was a lively buyers' scramble for the last of them.

By the end of 1939 more than 2,000,000 horsepower of turbine-generators were under construction by the General Electric Company or ready for delivery. Orders continued to come in during the following year, and in 1941, with the United States about to become an active participant in the war, reached the amazing total of more than 3,000,000 horsepower of turbine-generators and 1,250,000 horsepower of hydroelectric generators.

These generators gave American industry additional electric power at the time it was most urgently needed. They kept the machinery humming in the great automotive and aircraft factories. They powered and floodlighted the host of shipyards on both sides of the continent. They kept the rolls turning in the nation's steel mills. They supplied current for making vast quantities of aluminum, synthetic rubber, aviation gasoline, and other essential products.

About two-thirds of all the new generating capacity installed in the United States during the war years was equipment built by the General Electric Company. From the beginning of 1940 through 1945 the company produced for the electric-power industry more than a million and a quarter horsepower of turbine-generators a year. At the same time it produced an average of a third of a million horsepower of hydroelectric generating equipment a year.

BUILDING LAND TURBINES

Construction of the generators needed to meet the wartime power demands would have been a full-time job even if all of the company's production facilities had been available for this work. But they were not available. The Navy had already embarked on its huge expansion program and needed propulsion turbines for its new battleships, carriers, cruisers, and destroyers. So pressing was the need for this propulsion machinery that the Navy proposed that the company discontinue entirely the building of land turbines and concentrate on ship turbines.

Convinced that such a step would be harmful to the overall war effort, officials of the company went to Washington to present an alternative plan to the Navy Department. They pointed out that any power shortage resulting from inadequate generating capacity would seriously hamper the production of war equipment, which was just as important as propulsion turbines. A new turbine-parts shop was already under construction at the Schenectady Works to house additional facilities for the Navy's work. This building had been designed twice as large as was really needed. The company proposed that the excess space in the new building be equipped with additional machine tools and be utilized to make a limited number of land turbines. In this way, the Navy's program could proceed exactly as planned, and, at the same time, the company would provide equipment badly needed by the power industry.

With the assurance that its own program would be strictly adhered to, the Navy withdrew its objection to the building of land turbines. The War Production Board then set up a schedule for the building of two or three turbine-generators per month for the power industry. While the number of units involved in this program was small in comparison with the number of marine units, the individual machines averaged considerably larger. From the standpoint of horsepower, in fact, the land-turbine production amounted to almost a third as much as ship-turbine production.

After the manufacturing facilities had been set up, the company faced another dilemma. Its engineers were already swamped with design work on equipment for the Navy. Engineering personnel was lacking for the kind of detailed work ordinarily involved in the design of large land turbines. The only way these units could be produced was to follow basic designs that had already been worked out, making such minor modifications as were necessary in individual cases. As a result, some of the power companies received generating equipment slightly different from their ideal choice in normal times, but there were no complaints.

Securing materials for the construction of the land turbines did not at first present serious difficulties. The company had a moderate supply of castings and other component parts on hand, and they could be utilized for the manufacture of such equipment as the War Production Board authorized. As the war continued, this supply of material gradually became exhausted, and fewer land turbines could be built. During

1944 and 1945, production dropped to an average of only one and a half per month. By that time, however, the danger of a wartime power shortage had passed.

NEED FOR POWER TRANSFORMERS

Generating the increased amount of power required for war production was only the first part of the job. The additional power served no useful purpose until it began flowing into the actual manufacturing machinery. That spelled the need for a vast number of additional transformers to step up the generating voltage to a higher level for transmission and then to step it down again for utilization.

Before the war it had been the practice of the power industry to maintain a considerable reserve of extra, step-up transformer capacity. This reserve was quickly thrown into the production battle and virtually all the power industry's transformers were worked under heavy overload. In this way the task of getting the additional power on to the transmission lines was accomplished with a relatively small amount of new step-up transformer capacity. In a limited number of special instances General Electric built large transformers for power companies faced with unusual conditions, but the number was far below normal.

At the outer ends of the transmission lines the situation was more complicated. Many war plants were entirely new. Many of the established plants had larger power needs than ever before. This greatly changed the pattern of power distribution and necessitated the use of step-down transformers in countless new locations. For big industrial plants it became the wartime practice to run the high-tension transmission lines right to the factory and to step down the voltage by means of a unit substation on the premises. Huge quantities of transformers were needed for this purpose, and needed quickly.

For years these transformers had been made by the thousand at the Pittsfield Works. No radical changes in design being required to meet the wartime demands, the task was simply to turn out transformers of high quality on a shorter manufacturing cycle with smaller use of critical materials and with fewer man hours than ever before.

In 1940, the Transformer Division reached a higher manufacturing point than ever before. It was estimated then that a 10 per cent increase in volume would be entirely adequate for the next several years. Then came Pearl Harbor. In the following year the Transformer Division's output exceeded the 1940 figure by 85 per cent, and in 1944 reached a figure nearly 2½ times that of 1940. The importance of the equipment produced is indicated by the fact that the Pittsfield Works, the largest unit of the Transformer Division, was doing more than 98 per cent of its work on priorities of AA-3 or higher.

Early in the war the necessity arose of conserving critical materials, particularly in the power transformers in which large quantities of such materials were being used. To meet this situation it was decided to substitute noncritical materials in place of aluminum, copper, tin, etc., in practically every part other than current-carrying conductors.

In one instance "fine" silver was used in place of copper for the conductors in a group of large transformers. This was a rush job involving twelve 12,500-kva, 13,800-volt units urgently needed for an aluminum plant. Before the substitution was undertaken a thorough investigation was made of the characteristics of silver as compared with copper in the manufacturing processes of brazing, heating, casting wire-bars, hot-rolling wire bars, and cold-drawing into rectangular wire. The experiments brought to light no unexpected difficulties and the company decided to proceed with the plan. When completed, the transformers passed all tests without difficulty, met all guarantees, and were shipped on schedule.

The silver so utilized was and remained the property of the

United States Treasury. Because of its high value, extraordinary precautions were taken in the transportation and handling of the metal. Each carload, containing 50,000 pounds of silver worth about a quarter of a million dollars, traveled to the Transformer Division at Pittsfield escorted by U.S. Treasury guards armed with machine guns. Other Treasury guards were present throughout all fabricating operations. Since it was desired to recover the silver eventually, a plan was developed before construction started providing for later disassembly of the transformers and replacement of the silver by copper.

UNIT AND MOBILE SUBSTATIONS

Most helpful in meeting the need for transformers was the development and the widespread use of the relatively new unit substation. This, as its name suggests, was an assembly of one or more transformers with standard switchgear to form a completely metal-enclosed factory-built substation. Master unit substations ranged in capacity from 40,000 kva down to 750 kva. Smaller, load-center unit substations ranged from 2000 down to 100 kva.

To meet the power requirements of a new war-production plant, the practice was to install a master unit substation of appropriate size outside the plant and as many load-center unit substations as might be needed inside the plant. Prior to the development of the unit-substation plan, it was the usual practice to design a single substation to meet the particular needs of each individual plant, and to supply power to all the machinery by direct connection from this substation. This involved the use of a great deal of heavy, low-voltage cable and of costly, high-capacity switchgear because each circuit had the entire main transformer bank behind it.

Under the old conditions the power layout for a new plant was seldom completed until the building was nearly finished and the location of each machine definitely determined. Inevitably, there then elapsed a long period during which the transformer and switching equipment was being designed and manufactured. Despite its slowness this method had been followed in peacetime until the advent of the factory-assembled unit substation because it was considered to be the most economical way to make the installation.

Had this old practice been followed during the war, a large part of the nation's war-production facilities would not have been in operation until too late. Speed was essential, and the unit-substation plan provided speed. As soon as the size of a new factory had been agreed upon, and the general nature of the machinery had been determined, the necessary electric apparatus could be ordered. All that was necessary was to calculate the over-all power demand and to select a master unit substation of suitable size, together with an appropriate number of load-center unit substations. No time was lost making a detailed layout, designing special transformers, or worrying over what switchgear would be needed. The speed with which the process could be carried out was so great that in one instance a G-E engineer figured in 18 minutes the entire substation requirements of a new factory containing 15 acres of floor space. The order was placed and the equipment was in process of manufacture before the foundations of the structure had been completed.

The unit-substation plan proved of great value to electric utility companies as well as to industrial plants. Since the utilities were able to secure comparatively little new transformer equipment and many of them had to use their spares to meet regular daily load demands, they operated with virtually no emergency reserve. Under these conditions a mobile unit substation was a tremendous help. These units were mounted on high-speed highway trailers and could be hauled over the road at speeds up to 40 miles an hour. Upon arrival they could be hooked up quickly to assist an overloaded permanent substation, to provide temporary replacement of a damaged transformer, or to carry the load during overhaul of permanent equipment.

By concentrating on building a limited number of types of unit substations instead of specially designing and building substation equipment to fit a wide variety of different individual situations, it was possible to provide a far larger volume of power facilities. The aggregate capacity of all the unit substations built by the company during the war years was, in fact, about 5,000,000 kva. Undoubtedly these unit substations were a major factor in making it possible to say on V-J Day that nothing needed for the war effort had ever been delayed because the manufacturer could not get enough power to operate his machines.

17

Multiplying Production

AMONG THE THINGS that enabled the United States to produce an overwhelming supply of ships, planes, tanks, guns,
and other matériel of war, electric motors and electric welding were outstanding. The Axis powers never doubted the
ability of this nation to produce huge quantities of war
equipment eventually, but the speed at which it was done
upset all their calculations, for they had underestimated
American ingenuity in multiplying production.

ELECTRIC MUSCLES BY THE MILLION

Output of General Electric motors for industry had been
increasing steadily before the outbreak of the war. Small
sizes—below 1 horsepower—were made at Fort Wayne,
those of medium size—1 to 15 horsepower—were made at
the River Works, Lynn, while the large motors were made
at Schenectady, Erie, Fort Wayne, and Oakland. Even in
those days a substantial number of motors was being made
for the armed services. By far the largest part, however, was
for industry.

Developments never proceeded at a faster pace than during the years 1940 and 1941. Unfolding events brought to
the American people the growing realization that the coun-

try must prepare itself for a fighting war before time ran out and the Axis powers dominated the world. By quadrupling its motor production in 2 years General Electric was instrumental in powering the machine tools, pumps, compressors, fans, blowers, and other machinery essential to the production of war equipment.

Then the inevitable happened. The sheaf of urgent telegrams that arrived the morning after Pearl Harbor made one thing clear. Production of motors for industry would have to give way to production for the armed services. Every job not directly related to the war effort had to be sidetracked. Production had to be boosted to unimagined heights. But, despite the enormous demands of the armed forces there was never a day when standard industrial motors were not also in volume production to meet the greatly expanded needs for such motors on machine tools and other high-priority jobs. While this industrial production was but a small part of the company's total motor production the actual number of units was more than three-quarters of that made in peacetime, omitting household-refrigerator and washing-machine motors, and in integral horsepower sizes it exceeded peacetime production. For example, the number of general purpose alternating-current motors built during the war years was well over a million.

WORLD'S MOST POWERFUL MOTOR

Many special purpose motors were made, too. Among them were large numbers of special explosion-proof motors for ammunition factories, magnesium plants, oil refineries, and pipe lines.

The most powerful electric motor in the world—powerful enough to hoist a destroyer completely out of the water and up to the top of a 15-story building, all in a minute's time —was built for a new steel mill at Geneva, Utah. By applying its 7,000 horsepower at the comparatively low shaft speed of 25 revolutions per minute this giant direct-current motor developed more turning power than any other motor, either alternating or direct current, ever built. The motor had an over-all length of 44 feet, an outside diameter of 16 feet, and weighed nearly a million pounds. When installed, it stood 13 feet above the floor level. Nine freight cars were needed for its transportation from Schenectady to Geneva.

The motor was designed to drive a reversing rougher of a 132-inch, semicontinuous plate mill, capable of rolling steel plate in both directions. Slabs 6 to 8 inches thick and 60 inches wide were fed into the mill and emerged ¼ to ¾ inch thick and up to 127 inches wide. A single ¼-inch plate would weigh approximately 20,000 pounds and be approximately 200 feet long.

MAN-MADE HURRICANE

Electric motors to help simulate the atmospheric conditions encountered in high-altitude flying were built for the National Advisory Committee for Aeronautics' wind tunnel at Moffett Field, Calif. Two sets of fans working together created a wind that blew at a rate of more than 600 miles an hour. The motors were of 13,500 horsepower and operated at a speed of 1,800 revolutions per minute, giving them the highest peripheral speed of any motors ever built. Altogether, General Electric equipped a total of thirteen wind tunnels at various locations with drives ranging in size from 750 to 27,000 horsepower.

120,000 REVOLUTIONS PER MINUTE

In contrast to the huge motors for steel mills and wind tunnels was an exceptionally small motor rated at 3 horsepower, but weighing only 7 pounds, as compared with the conventional 3-horsepower motor, which weighs 105 pounds.

It was so small that the entire motor could fit into the palm of a person's hand and its rotor was scarcely larger than a man's thumb.

Operating at the record-breaking speed of 120,000 revolutions per minute, this tiny motor was used for grinding the ball-bearing raceways of airplane instruments. It was water cooled, using about ½ gallon of water a minute, and was equipped with an oil-mist lubricating type of bearing. Tests, including a continuous run of 8 hours, proved its ability to perform with great reliability despite its small dimensions.

EXPEDITING TANK CONSTRUCTION

Throughout the war, welding made an outstanding contribution to the volume and speed of American production. It was employed in making all kinds of tools and weapons, in the construction of factories where these tools and weapons were manufactured, and in building the ships that carried them overseas.

Up to 1941 the United States had not built any welded tanks. The Germans had welded tanks, though they used carefully mortised and fitted joints, and hence did not rely wholly upon the welding. When Rommel invaded Egypt, the superiority of his welded tanks gave him an advantage over the British riveted tanks, which had one great drawback. Even if a shell did not penetrate the armor, the impact frequently sheared off the rivet heads and sent them flying inside the tank, causing injury and death to members of the crew.

After the United States entered the war there was no time to make tanks by the careful machining methods the Germans used. Tanks had to be welded, and the welding had to be good enough to stand up under severe punishment. After many experiments a new type of welding electrode was developed and all-welded tanks began rolling off the assembly lines in every section of the country.

In the fall of 1942, Marshal Rommel was getting ready at El Alamein to continue his drive to the Suez Canal. Then on October 23, the stillness of the desert night was suddenly broken by the wail of Scottish bagpipes, followed immediately by such a deafening thunder of artillery as the desert had never heard before. The reinforced British Eighth Army, provided with thousands of airplanes and a huge fleet of all-welded "General Sherman" tanks, brought from America around the Cape of Good Hope, was launching its long-awaited counterstroke.

In less than 2 weeks the German line was completely shattered and Rommel was in full retreat. As he made his way back over the long, tortuous road across Libya a pack of snarling General Shermans was constantly at his heels. They followed him through Tunisia. They crossed into Sicily and then to the Italian mainland. "No praise can be too high for these tanks," said General Montgomery, "and for the factories and workers who have made them."

WELDED SHIPS FOR WAR

War's demand for speed prompted the widespread adoption of welding in ship construction, just as it did in tank construction. The first all-welded U.S. merchant ship was launched about 10 years before the war, and this method of construction developed fairly rapidly in the building of the merchant vessels turned out by American shipyards. Four out of five of the wartime merchant ships were welded. The Navy was somewhat slower to adopt the practice, but at the height of the war effort the smaller Navy vessels and landing craft were being welded throughout and the larger vessels were about 70 per cent welded.

Fortunately for the success of the welded-ship program, welding equipment well suited for use in ship construction had been developed before the war. The outstanding characteristic of this equipment was that it was designed to take care of numerous welding operations of short duration in a small area with minimum power consumption. Its ability to do this was not of much value in ordinary industrial operations, but it exactly fitted the needs of the hard-pressed shipbuilding industry. All that was necessary was for the company to speed up the production of units of existing design. This was done so effectively that the company was able to supply enough equipment to meet the needs of some 30,000 ship welders.

The application of welding to ship construction presented certain problems in the beginning. A few of the welded ships developed cracks that caused grave anxiety. Investigations were made quickly. They showed that the welds themselves with rare exceptions were well made and equal in strength to the surrounding metal. On the other hand, it was found that some of the features of design and methods employed in fabricating the welded ships created an accumulation of residual stresses in the steel, which, when additional stresses were imposed from various causes at sea, produced failure of the structure. Changes in design and production methods were promptly made to avoid the dangerous residual stresses. New procedures were established for inspection as the work progressed. Construction of welded ships proceeded, and failures were almost entirely eliminated.

Welding saved both manpower and metal in shipbuilding. It helped to cut 25 to 50 per cent from the time ordinarily required to turn out a completed vessel. One welder could do the work of a four-man riveting team. Welding produced a high ratio of strength to weight. Beyond any doubt it was the most essential factor in the successful completion of the world's greatest shipbuilding program.

THE "BIG INCH"

Construction of the famous "Big Inch" pipe line in record-breaking time would have been impossible without electric welding. Before the war 93 per cent of the oil used on the Eastern seaboard of the United States was brought in from the Gulf of Mexico by tanker. A big pipe line had been discussed from time to time but nothing had been done about it. The outbreak of war in Europe caused many of the coastal tankers to be diverted to carrying oil overseas. This ship diversion cut the supplies available in the Eastern states, but still no definite action was taken to build the pipe line.

When the United States became an active participant in the war, the remaining oil tankers shuttling back and forth between the oil fields and Atlantic ports began to fall victim with startling rapidity to the attacks of German submarines. The situation was rapidly becoming critical, so it was decided to proceed with the building of a pipe line. Known to oil men as the "Big Inch," this pipe line was laid out over a 1,254-mile route from the Texas oil fields to the Middle Atlantic seacoast.

When steel plates could not be obtained for making fabricated pipe, it was decided to use the largest available size of seamless pipe. This was of 24-inch diameter, ⅜ inch thick, and came in 38-foot lengths. Four pieces were welded together to form a 150-foot section. These were laid end to end on the ground alongside a trench in which the pipe was ultimately buried. Sections were then welded together in assemblies of varying length, depending on the topography.

Altogether, more than a hundred contractors were engaged on the project, employing some 16,000 workers. Progress was made at a rate of about 6 miles a day. The eastern terminal at Phoenixville, Pa., was reached a few days short of a year from the date when the first weld was made at Longview, Tex. Through this line were delivered 300,000 barrels (12,600,000 gallons) of oil per day—as much as a fleet of 77 average tankers could carry in normal times on the route through the Gulf of Mexico and up the coast to Philadelphia. As its contribution to the "Big Inch," General

Electric supplied a large amount of welding equipment for construction purposes and most of the big pump motors to keep the oil flowing steadily up hill and down at a rate of 4 miles per hour.

"OPERATION PLUTO"

Another spectacular wartime pipe line was built across the English Channel from Britain to France. As the highly mechanized American and British armies drove relentlessly across France and into the heart of Germany, the world wondered where their tanks and trucks and self-propelled guns were getting the gasoline necessary to keep going. The answer lay in "Operation Pluto"—the construction of a 70-mile "pipe line under the ocean" from the Isle of Wight to Cherbourg on the coast of Normandy. Twenty separate 3-inch pipes were laid across the channel, carrying more than a million gallons of gasoline per day. The total mileage of pipe used for this undertaking was about the same as that for the "Big Inch," and the problems of construction were even more difficult.

The idea for this pipe line across the English Channel was born back in April, 1942, during a conversation between Geoffrey Lloyd, British Minister of Petroleum Warfare, and Admiral Lord Louis Mountbatten, in charge of commando operations. They were discussing the problems connected with the invasion of the continent of Europe, which everybody realized must eventually be undertaken if Germany was to be defeated.

"How can the Ministry of Petroleum Warfare most effectively assist the invasion?" Lloyd asked the admiral.

"You might lay a pipe line across the channel," Mountbatten replied.

Eminent British engineers were consulted. Most of them thought the job was impossible. But A. C. Hartley, chief engineer of the Anglo-Iranian Oil Company, said he believed it could be done by making a pipe like a submarine electric-power cable, omitting the insulation and the conductors. Cable of this kind had already been built to withstand considerable pressures, and he thought the same principles could be applied in building a really, high-pressure pipe.

A short, experimental 2-inch pipe line was built and laid in the Bristol channel in December, 1942. Results were so encouraging that it was decided to proceed with the project, but to use a pipe of 3-inch diameter instead. Orders were immediately placed with a number of British cable manufacturers in anticipation of D Day. Their plants, however, were in fairly vulnerable locations along the Thames estuary, and bombs from the German *Luftwaffe* occasionally dropped uncomfortably close to them. The "Pluto" project was considered so important that authorities decided that some of the pipe should be manufactured in the United States.

General Electric, because of its technical knowledge and experience in cable making, was given the job of producing 20 miles of the new pipe line. Since the undersea pipe had to be able to withstand tremendous pressure—1,200 pounds per square inch as compared with about 10 to 15 pounds in ordinary submarine cables—entirely new methods of production had to be set up.

The pipe itself was of extruded lead, with a 3-inch inside diameter and a wall thickness of about $2/10$ inch. This was given an outside coating of asphalt, and then wrapped with four layers of steel tape. A second coating of asphalt was applied and the pipe was then armored with galvanized steel wire. More asphalt and two layers of jute provided the outer covering. When completed the pipe had an outside diameter of 4.6 inches and weighed slightly more than 20 pounds per foot.

A production line 400 feet long was set up. The pipe was made in 2,300-foot lengths, which were later joined together. A new, electronic-controlled welder and annealer was installed for welding the steel tape and wire. To prevent collapse of the lead pipe during armoring, it was kept under an inside pressure of 40 pounds per square inch during this process. Work proceeded on a 24-hour basis, 7 days a week. Finished pipe was carefully coiled on gondola cars rebuilt for this express purpose.

The cable manufactured at Schenectady was shipped by rail to Yonkers, where it was spliced into continuous lengths sufficient to reach across the English Channel and placed on a vessel for transportation to England. Special British cable-laying ships had meanwhile been made ready. Shortly after D Day they started across the channel, unreeling the under-seas pipe. Storms hampered the work and more than once threatened disaster, but they persevered. As soon as the end had been made secure on the French coast, pumping stations concealed in an ancient English port, in an amusement park, and in an ice cream factory began supplying precious fuel to the forces on the continent.

Altogether, twelve parallel lines of this cable pipe were laid, along with eight lines of 3-inch welded steel pipe. General Eisenhower was high in his praise of the job, and the German Marshal von Runstedt is reported to have said that the tremendous supply of gasoline available to the armies of the United Nations was a major factor in the defeat of Germany.

18

New Equipment and Materials

NEW USES OF ELECTRICAL EQUIPMENT and new materials developed in connection with the making of electrical equipment played significant roles in expediting war production. To the engineers of G.E.'s Air Conditioning Department, for example, fell the task of creating a stratosphere on earth, of reproducing for test purposes at sea level the pressures and temperatures encountered by a high-flying military plane. Sudden, severe temperature changes were everyday experience in air warfare. A plane could leave the hot floor of the desert at a temperature well over 100 degrees Fahrenheit, and climb in an incredibly short time to an altitude of 30,000 to 40,000 feet where the temperature was 50 to 110 degrees below zero. At these low temperatures natural rubber crumbles into a granular powder, navigation instruments lose their accuracy, ordinary lubricants congeal into a gummy wax, and even radio sets can no longer be relied upon. For these reasons every part of a new plane designed for high-altitude flying had to be tested thoroughly and precisely under conditions approximating those of actual flight.

CREATING A STRATOSPHERE ON EARTH

Existing types of air-conditioning and refrigeration equipment required ingenious design changes in order to reproduce the desired stratosphere effect. The company's engineers found that by using more effective insulating materials, combined with two- and three-stage refrigeration systems, the test chamber could be brought down to a much lower temperature than that achieved in prior practice. In hundreds of these testing chambers, G-E equipment maintained conditions ranging from humid tropical heat to the extreme cold prevailing at 40,000 feet, with a change from one extreme to the other proceeding as rapidly as the rate of climb or descent of an airplane.

Through experience gained in these subzero testing chambers, special synthetic rubbers were developed to withstand the conditions that natural rubber could not endure. Special wax-free lubricants were produced, which did not congeal in extreme cold. Navigation instruments and radio systems were designed that were constantly reliable.

Stringent tests were also conducted to find ways of prolonging the life of carbon brushes on the electric motors and generators on airplanes. These brushes, developed for peacetime on the ground or at moderate altitudes, gave reasonably satisfactory wear in early airplanes, but as ceilings were raised during the war, brush life grew definitely too short, only 7 hours as against several hundred hours previously obtained.

Fortunately, it had already been shown by the G.E. Research Laboratory that low humidity meant short brush life, so the basic cause of the trouble was clear. Suitable chambers were constructed for exact control of altitude, temperature, and humidity for experimental testing of brushes. Through their use, a way was found to make brushes that would have a life equivalent to that obtained under moderate altitude conditions.

LIGHTING FOR WAR INDUSTRY

Electric lighting played an outstanding part in facilitating war production. When the lights went out in the homes and

Rotor for one of the many big land turbine-generators
which G.E. built to supply power for the war effort.

More power for industry—a new 80,000-kilowatt turbine-generator joins one already in operation in a large eastern power station.

*Housing for one of four vertical waterwheel generators for instal-
lation at Shasta dam.*

New power transformers to increase substation capacity.

Installing oil-filled bushing in a large G.E. power transformer.

Load-center unit-substations like this saved valuable time in laying out power supply for war manufacturing plants.

Mobile unit-substations supplies vital electric power during temporary emergency.

Largest electric motor ever built—7000-horsepower machine for semi-continuous steel platemill.

World's fastest motor—weighing only seven pounds, this machine for grinding ball bearing raceways developed three horsepower at 120,000 revolutions per minute.

Built by welding—SS African Comet, the first passenger vessel to be so fabricated.

Welding was essential to speed in tank construction, and produced equipment that was unexcelled in any army.

Traction bars being welded to floor plates of a tank-carrying invasion barge.

Welding joints for the "Big Inch" pipe line, laid over a 1254-mile route in record breaking time.

Wire armor for "Pluto," the 3-inch fuel "Pipe line under the ocean," or more accurately under the English channel.

Loading last car carrying a five-mile shipment of 3-inch fuel pipe.

factories of Europe because of the war, they were turned on in larger numbers than ever in the United States. Near the Atlantic and Pacific coasts the general level of night illumination was reduced a little by the dimout, but elsewhere throughout the country lights blazed more brightly than before.

Factory-wise American industry turned night into day. If the fighting tools that were so urgently needed were to be at the right place at the right time in the right quantities, industry could not wait for giant new factories to be built. The existing plants, shops, and office buildings had to carry a tremendously increased load and operate 24 hours a day. To a considerable extent the fluorescent lamp, perfected a short time before by General Electric, provided the answer to the problem of satisfactory lighting for nightwork.

Time and again, as the war continued, government and industry took their problems to Nela Park, General Electric's great lamp establishment near Cleveland. How could accidents be prevented at critical machines? How could the interior of machine-gun barrels be inspected accurately? How could spoilage of precious materials be reduced? How would it be possible to increase the efficiency of the "graveyard" shift in manufacturing plants? How could a mammoth outdoor shipyard be lighted for round-the-clock production? To answer these and similar questions, G.E.'s Lamp Department engineers, with their intimate knowledge of efficient lighting, transferred their whole attention from the problems of civilian life to the problems created by the war.

The entire sales force was diverted from its normal work to a vast program of lighting assistance to industry. Under the flag of "Bomber Builders," they went into industrial plants to render service to war production—not knowing whether, to remove lighting bottlenecks, they were going to suggest merely cleaning of lighting fixtures, or relocating fixtures, or the use of paint, or the addition of new lighting equipment.

They rated themselves in terms of the numbers of man-hours required to build bombers and when it was all added up, they gave nearly a million and a half workers better seeing conditions in plants turning out war equipment and supplies. This achievement provided upwards of 88,000,000 additional man-hours a year for the nation's war-production effort—the equivalent of finding nearly 50,000 additional workers for war industry. Translated into terms of Flying Fortresses or Liberators, it was the equivalent of adding nearly a thousand of those huge four-engined bombers a year to the nation's striking power.

Lighting needs were, of course, the chief cause for the huge wartime demands for lamps. But they were by no means the only cause. In many war plants large numbers of infrared drying lamps were used to evaporate moisture on unpainted parts of war equipment and to bake the paint on jeeps, tanks, Army trucks, guns, and other apparatus in one-tenth the average time required by ordinary methods. In one instance it cut the drying time on airplane instrument cases from 6 hours to 27 minutes.

Drying lamps were used also to speed the processing of photographic films and to dry the glue on envelope flaps. They were employed for expanding metals in making airplane parts. In the food industry they were utilized for dehydrating foods to save tin cans and jar rings. Again and again they made it possible to break industrial bottlenecks and speed up production.

Photomicrographic lamps were another important aid to industry. They were in constant use in factory laboratories as part of the intricate apparatus used to analyze the grain structure of metals. On inspection lines they projected magnified images of small parts for accurate checking. In a multitude of ways they were vital to the perfection in manufacture that was needed to win the war.

INCREASED DEMAND FOR PLASTICS

Among the new materials that helped to speed the war effort, plastics were outstanding. Before the war the word "plastics" had been almost unknown to the average American, but it leaped quickly into general use as scarcities began to develop in strategic materials for which plastics could effectively be used as replacements. For many purposes, in fact, plastics were found to be definitely superior to the materials customarily employed. Frequently, an article made of plastics proved to be simpler, more durable, lower in cost, lighter in weight, and more uniform in quality than a similar article made of other materials.

Plastics comprise a group of structural materials which have for their active ingredients synthetic organic elements, and which, in the process of manufacture, undergo pressing or molding under conditions of controlled temperature and pressure. They can be molded into almost any desired shape, or they can be rolled into thin sheets like paper or cloth and made up into standard items such as sheets, tubes, or rods. Their physical properties give them an extremely wide field of usefulness. For example, metal is strong, wood is light in weight, and glass is transparent, but certain plastics are the only materials that have all of these qualities in combination.

Under the dynamic compulsion of war, plastics assumed a position of unprecedented importance. The great demand soon put plastics on the list of critical materials—available only on high priority for essential needs. Hundreds of manufacturers of consumer items, unable to obtain the metals they ordinarily used, turned to General Electric, the largest producer of molded plastics parts in the country, only to discover that plastics had been restricted to war uses and could no longer be employed for the making of electric appliances and other household products.

MOLDED PARTS FOR PLANES AND SHIPS

Many plastic molding compounds were developed to meet special conditions. An example was their use for radio loop-antenna housings for bombers. Formerly these housings consisted of a wood frame covered with cloth. The entire assembly was held together by an adhesive. This construction had many disadvantages. It was slow and costly to build and did not lend itself to mass production. The finished assembly was too brittle to stand up under the terrific beating it had to take from rain, ice, snow, sun, and extremes of temperature.

It was suggested to General Electric that a more satisfactory housing might be made of a plastic material. Development work was started at once. When early models were tested, they stood up under wind, rain, ice, sun, and extremes of temperature, but the plastics material used gave unforeseen trouble. It released ammonia that corroded the metal fittings. Also it did not give sufficient safeguard against the building up of static electricity, and too much static would interfere seriously with radio reception.

General Electric's engineers corrected the corrosion condition by replacing the two-stage phenolic resin with an ammonia-free one-stage resin in the molding compound. Then it was found that the addition of graphite to the molding compound would give the degree of conductivity necessary to prevent hazardous static build-up in the molded-plastics parts.

The fabric filler used in this ammonia-free, graphite-added molding compound were cuttings of fine cotton twill uniform shirts supplied by military tailors. These "shirttails" had to be carefully selected, because textiles which had been waterproofed for tropical use failed to absorb resin. This special molding compound made the plastics loop-antenna housing acceptable, and the company supplied tens of thousands of them for bombers.

Use of plastics was a tremendous timesaver in the manufacture of control blocks for variable-pitch propellers for airplanes. These blocks were of curved shape, containing many metal contact points to transmit electric power to the pitch-changing mechanism that gave the pilot control over the angle of propeller "bite." Previous methods of making the blocks involved complicated boring or punching operations and laborious insertion of the metal contact points. With plastics the whole assembly could be molded in a matter of minutes. Not only did this process save time and money, but it also produced better parts.

In shipbuilding the use of stern tube bearings made of plastics overcame what might have been a serious bottleneck. For a century, lignum vitae, one of the hardest and heaviest known woods, had been used for the bearing where the propeller shaft passes through the hull of the ship at the stern. Water lubricated the bearings made in this way. The only trouble was that lignum vitae had to be obtained from the tropics, and the quality of the wood was not uniform.

Some years before the war General Electric began making stern tube bearings laminated of phenolic-treated heavy cotton twill fabrics, which were molded into long staves. These staves, not unlike thick straight barrel staves, were fitted lengthwise into a brass housing in the stern of the ship. They were beveled to provide channels next to the shaft for water lubrication. This took the guesswork out of making stern tube bearings as all the plastics staves were uniform in quality. Under the greatly expanded wartime shipbuilding program, G.E. made thousands of these staves for the Navy and the Merchant Marine.

At the peak of the war effort, General Electric plastic plants were producing more than 14,500 different items for war use. Besides the radio and radar housings, propeller pitch blocks, and stern tube bearings, there was a host of small parts and devices.

When a battleship went into action, a loudspeaker system was used to broadcast orders throughout the vessel. Most of these loudspeakers had G-E plastics diaphragms, specially designed to take the shock from the firing of the ship's big guns. Telephone hand sets, which had to be made with great precision, were built of plastics. The Navy tested them by dropping them down a 6-foot chute at an 80-degree angle. Barrage balloons, to protect invasion beachheads, were equipped with relief valves made of plastics. Airplane control dials, charts, and instruction plates were produced from plastics. They were engraved, printed, or stamped in colors, or embossed—whichever way would give the most satisfactory service. They were light, easy to read, tough, durable, and resistant to weather.

Despite the tremendous volume and variety of its plastics production General Electric was its own largest customer. Practically every department used plastics parts in the apparatus and equipment it made. Laminated plastics collars and cylinder coils were used for transformers, bushings for motors, cases for meters and instruments, handles, knobs, cams, rocker arms, and switchgear housings for electrical-control equipment, panels, coils, relay blocks, and control parts for turbine-generators, and thousands of other items for other purposes.

DEVELOPMENT OF SILICONE RUBBER

Time was when no elastic substance existed that was suitable for use as gasket material at high temperatures. This created a serious problem for the armed forces. When Navy searchlights, for example, were used to direct the fire of guns at night, they had to be as close as possible to the battery. Every time a gun was fired the searchlight was jarred and shaken. The lens, therefore, had to be mounted with some sort of shock absorber to prevent breakage. But this shock absorber had to be of a material that could resist the tremendous heat of the light's electric arc.

At first the Navy used asbestos for searchlight gaskets. These withstood the heat all right, but they lacked resiliency. A good many searchlight lenses were shattered. Some more satisfactory material was badly needed.

For a number of years General Electric chemists had been conducting research in the curious chemical compounds known as "silicones." A principal constituent of these compounds is silicon, the element present in such common things as glass and sand. Chemically speaking, silicon is quite similar to carbon, a major ingredient of natural and synthetic rubber. Both silicon and carbon can form long, chainlike molecules called "polymers." Silicon polymers, however, have much greater thermal stability than carbon polymers.

Making use of this characteristic of silicon, the company's Research Laboratory developed a new material called "silicone rubber," having many of the qualities of natural rubber and certain additional advantages. Silicone rubber can be compressed between metal plates to two-thirds of its original thickness, held that way for an extended period of time at a high temperature, and, when released, return to 90 per cent of its former dimensions. Its elastic properties are retained over a temperature range from 55 degrees below zero Fahrenheit to as high as 572 degrees. Moreover, it is unaffected by numerous other conditions that cause natural rubber to deteriorate.

These qualities of silicone rubber made it an ideal material to meet the Navy's and Army's need for searchlight shock absorbers. It was of great value, too, as gasket material for the turbosuperchargers in which gases from the exhaust, at a temperature well over a thousand degrees, are used to drive the turbine. Neither natural rubber nor synthetic rubber was satisfactory as gasket material for these superchargers, but silicone rubber was found to perform perfectly for long periods of high-altitude flying.

Along with silicone rubber the company developed numerous types of silicone resins, oils, and greases, characterized by being remarkably stable under a wide variety of conditions and temperatures. The silicone oils proved extremely useful as lubricants on timing motors, as damping fluids in voltage regulators, and as lubricants in optical devices for aircraft armament and for ball bearings on low-temperature motors for aircraft gun-control devices. The major wartime use for silicone resins was in the insulation of electric equipment for aircraft use. Because of their heat-resisting qualities it was possible to make the equipment much smaller and lighter than would otherwise have been possible.

Another outgrowth of silicon research was "Dri-Film," a water repellent. One of its important war applications was on insulators in communication equipment. Airplanes going swiftly from high to low altitudes often found that humidity changes caused condensation of moisture on the ceramic insulators of their radios, interfering seriously with the operation of the equipment. Conventional materials permitted moisture to condense in continuous films, covering so large a portion of the insulating surface that resistance was almost entirely lost. On a part treated with Dri-Film, however, the moisture formed into separated droplets.

Dri-Film was used also in making the canisters of gas masks. These contained corrugated paper disks to screen out dust and smoke particles from the absorbent charcoal. The disk had to be porous to permit breathing. If it became wet, as might easily happen in landing operations, water clogged the pores and made the mask virtually useless. Many materials were tried in an attempt to find one that would make the paper repel water without clogging it. Dri-Film proved to be the answer. In one test, an officer of the Chemical War-fare Service put on a treated mask and submerged himself to a depth of several feet in a pool of water without impairing the mask's efficiency.

Dri-Film also proved its effectiveness as a water repellent to maintain the clarity of glass under storm conditions. It was approved for treatment of glass on landing barges and tank-periscope windows.

Much of the wartime electric equipment had to operate at high voltages and frequencies, as well as under severe conditions of temperature, humidity, vibration, and altitude. Normally the windings of such equipment would have been protected by immersion in a liquid dielectric, but size and weight limitations on war equipment required that it operate dry. Conventional insulating varnishes were found to be inadequate. Engineers of the G.E. Research Laboratory, however, had been working on the development of a new group of fluids known as "Permafil," which harden into solids without evaporation and hence without formation of voids. These fluids, developed to meet differing conditions, were produced in quantity by the Chemical Department and proved superior to conventional varnishes for high-voltage applications.

Before the war the Navy had been using linseed oil and varnish paints, but something that would dry faster and have greater durability was needed to speed up ship construction and keep ships in service longer before they needed repainting. General Electric's Chemical Department convinced the Navy that the answer was an alkyd resin paint. Competitive tests were held and Glyptal was found best. As a result the Navy prepared new specifications written around such a paint.

TUNGSTEN AND MOLYBDENUM

Demands for tungsten and molybdenum increased steadily as the war progressed. As the producer of about three-quarters of the nation's high-purity tungsten and as the nation's greatest user of these metals, General Electric was already conducting extensive research in connection with their production before the war. The company had developed ways to process the "off-grade" ores that had to take the places of those coming from Burma and China sources when the latter could no longer be obtained. Thus, when the war came, there were available in adequate quantity powders for cutting tools and dies, rods for welding, carbide cores for armor-piercing shells, rods for airplane spark plugs, and wire and rods for electronic and X-ray tubes as well as filament for lamps.

When the war ended, the War Production Board took occasion to thank the company for its cooperation in meeting the wartime demands for tungsten and molybdenum. "The Cleveland Wire Works in particular," said the War Production Board, "has set an outstanding production record which has played an important part in achieving final victory."

19

Testing and Measuring

IN ADDITION TO speeding quantity production, electricity was also a major factor contributing to the quality. Electric testing and measuring devices ranged from the huge 2-million volt X-ray machine down to the world's smallest oscillograph. They provided information of inestimable value concerning the physical properties of war equipment and also concerning its behavior under service conditions.

The nature of the discovery of X ray by Wilhelm Konrad Roentgen back in 1895 foreshadowed its later extensive use in industry. For a long time, however, the possible uses of X ray in industry were more or less neglected in the popular enthusiasm about what it could do in medicine.

What Roentgen discovered was that rays coming from a vacuum tube would pass through a seemingly impervious shield and affect photographic plates on the far side. Because he did not know the nature of this new kind of ray he borrowed the mathematical symbol X for the unknown quantity and called it the X ray.

On this side of the Atlantic a young lad, William David Coolidge, studying electrical engineering at the Massachusetts Institute of Technology, became interested in Roentgen's discovery. He began some experiments of his own which were later continued in the General Electric Research Laboratory. After years of arduous work they showed the way to the development of a more powerful vacuum tube, which marked the beginning of a new chapter in X-ray history.

RADIOGRAPHY IN INDUSTRY

The first industrial use of X ray in the United States began in 1922 when transformers, controls, and tubes reached a degree of perfection that made possible the employment of relatively high voltages. This proved especially useful in the examination of iron and steel castings, which frequently contained cracks and blowholes invisible on the surface. The traditional way of testing for hidden defects was by breaking a certain number of castings and examining them, but this procedure was much like striking a match merely to see if it is a good one.

Sometimes a casting shows signs of possible faults on the surface, and the engineer is in doubt whether he is confronted by superficial markings or apparently trivial defects that will eventually widen into large fissures or cavities. Many important and expensive castings have been scrapped because the engineer dared not risk using them.

X rays provided industry with a means of seeing into and learning a great deal about the interior of castings and other articles without destroying or harming them. During World War II, General Electric X-ray Corporation supplied more than 75 per cent of the industrial X-ray equipment used in navy yards, naval research laboratories, government arsenals, and plants of manufacturers of war equipment.

EXAMINATION OF CASTINGS

The war demanded castings of extraordinary size and thickness. At the same time there was imperative need for cutting the reject rate and for keeping close check on the results of increased speed in production. High-voltage X ray was of inestimable value in meeting these needs. It offered a nondestructive method of testing products for such faults as blowholes, tears, shrinkage cavities, foreign matter, and cracks which could not be detected by the keenest eye, but which constituted a hazard in war equipment. In some instances the use of X ray cut the time required for metal inspection to one-tenth what it formerly had been. Of particular importance was the fact that with it castings and forgings could be examined before being machined, thus saving a tremendous amount of machine tool time that might otherwise have been wasted on defective material.

At an airplane plant near Chicago, an X-ray unit checked 40 cylindrical bronze bearings simultaneously, cutting down inspection time from 5 hours to 10 minutes. A propeller company in Ohio speeded up its inspection 300 per cent with a 400,000-volt X-ray unit, which checked three airplane blades every 3 minutes. At one turbosupercharger plant in Wisconsin, engineers radiographed 36 of these wheels in 40 minutes. Any slag, cracks, or internal defects in the welded materials were easily discernible on the X-ray film.

A Detroit manufacturer used sixteen different types of X-ray units to speed up production of war materials—parts for tanks, bombers, gun mounts, armor plate, aircraft engines, turbosuperchargers, truck and jeep engines, and gun directors. At one time during the war period, X-ray departments in that plant employed 125 people, and the company maintained an apprentice training school to teach civilians how to operate the equipment and to process films.

This company used a million-volt X-ray unit to inspect crankshafts for a 500-horsepower tank engine, and also heavy castings for a light armored car. Every 250-pound crankshaft built into a tank engine underwent radiographic inspection with the million-volt unit. It took only 17 minutes to radiograph 12 crankshafts.

Million-volt radiography performed notably at one large

foundry, where the apparatus was installed late in 1942. Prior to that the foundry had produced some 50,000 castings from which gears were to be cut. Of this quantity, 14 per cent had been returned as scrap due to real or suspected defects. On the first 75,000 castings made after X-ray examinations were instituted to determine how many suspected castings were actually defective, only 1¼ per cent had to be returned as scrap. On another large job the proportion of rejections dropped from 21 per cent before X ray was used to six-tenths of one per cent afterward. On these two jobs alone the foundry saved more than $13,000. X ray also permitted much more rapid and accurate analysis of the causes of the defects found.

Navy yards found X-ray units almost indispensable. Million-volt machines operated day and night during the war at Norfolk, Philadelphia, Pearl Harbor, and Boston. At the Philadelphia Navy Yard, where battleships like the U.S.S. *New Jersey* and the U.S.S. *Wisconsin* were built in record time, the million-volt unit inspected steam-pressure castings weighing from 200 to 1,500 pounds. It found any defects and showed them on the developed film.

Engineers at the Philadelphia Navy Yard placed twenty castings in a circle around the target of a million-volt unit, and all were radiographed simultaneously with a single 2-minute exposure. Portable X-ray units inspected welds in high-pressure pipes carrying steam from one end of the ship to the other.

One day in the summer of 1944, a long-distance telephone call came to the G.E. X-ray Corporation in Chicago from the Navy Yard at Portsmouth, Va. "We need a million-volt X-ray machine in a hurry for inspection of 8-inch steel armor plate," the officer explained. "If you can supply the machine, we'll send a plane up for it." A unit of the desired type was located and hastily made ready for shipment. Next day a big Navy transport plane arrived from Portsmouth at the Chicago airport. The 2,500-pound X-ray unit was loaded aboard and the plane started back for Portsmouth. Six hours later it was being trucked into the Navy Yard. Ordinarily, the time required for transportation would have been at least 3 days. Thus the sending of the machine by air affected a substantial saving of production time on vital Navy equipment.

TESTING SHELLS AND FUSES

During the course of the war nearly fifty of these million-volt units were made by the company and placed in service in war plants from coast to coast. Three were purchased by the Ordnance Department of the Army. One of these was used at the Milan, Tenn., Ordnance Center, one at the Ravenna Ordnance Plant, Apco, Ohio, and the third at the Iowa Ordnance Plant at Burlington.

The X-ray installation at Milan, designed by the G.E. Research Laboratory and used principally for the inspection of 155-millimeter shells, was almost entirely automatic. Its job began right after the shells were filled with TNT. The explosive was poured into the shell casings at high temperature. In the cooling process that followed, it shrank in volume, the same as many metals do. The operator had to exercise extreme care in pouring lest the casing be incompletely filled. This cavitation, if it occurred, was easily spotted when the shell was radiographed.

Through the use of the X-ray equipment, it was possible for the first time in history to inspect the shell without destroying it. Moreover, the inspectors were given a much wider range of sampling. They could radiograph 700 shells out of a lot of 20,000 and, from the developed films, obtain a much more accurate analysis than was possible by visual inspection. Another important advantage was that if any defective shells were found among the 700 samples, it was not necessary to throw away the whole lot. X ray made it possible to radiograph every doubtful shell speedily and to separate the defective ones from the good.

On this inspection job, four girls worked outside the big exposure room that housed the X-ray equipment. With the aid of an air hoist, one girl took the 155-millimeter shells from a truck and loaded them into the fifty cubicles of a motorized ring. Another girl took a special frame, previously loaded with X-ray film, and placed it behind each shell as it was put on the ring. This operator also stamped the shell with the number corresponding to the number on the frame and recorded the shell and film numbers so that the pertinent information could be correlated later.

The shell and loaded film frame entered the exposure room on the motorized ring by passing through an aperture in the concrete wall. Within the room, the X-ray radiation produced a radiographic image of the shell and its contents on the film.

A third operator removed the frame after the shell had passed through the exposure room, and marked the shell "X-rayed." The fourth girl, working with an air hoist, removed the shell from the ring.

The equipment was capable of radiographing 3,300 shells every 24 hours of operation, allowing for nonoperating time and shift changes.

After the film frames left the exposure room, they were taken to a darkroom near by. Girl operators opened the frames and removed the X-ray film. By means of a special loading board, they fastened two of the special-size films on each developing hanger. An overhead conveyer system took the loaded hangers to the automatic developing unit where another operator placed them in the magazine of the film-processing machine. Meanwhile, the frames from which the films had been removed were pushed across the table to another operator who reloaded them with new X-ray film,

Stratosphere on earth—chamber where high-altitude pressures and temperatures were reproduced for testing aircraft instruments.

Turning night into day—floodlights permitted shipyards to work around the clock.

Fluorescent lighting to speed production in a bomber plant.

Special lamp for inspecting parachutes.

*A pill machine which presses molding compound
into pellets of pre-determined weight.*

*Racks of radomes—aircraft
radar antenna housings
made of plastics.*

Bending silicone rubber at 60 degrees below zero. Natural rubber would break if bent at such a temperature.

Silicone rubber gasket for Navy searchlight—designed to withstand high temperature and severe vibration.

Million-volt X-ray used for examination of large castings.

Checking power in grenade fuses with special X-ray machine developed by General Electric.

X-ray equipment for rapid inspection of 155-mm shells.

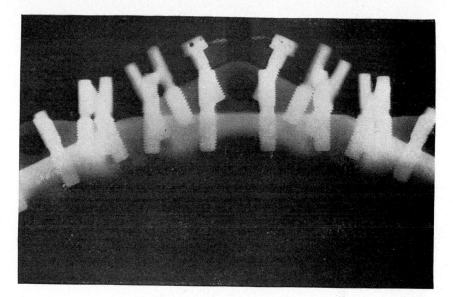

Radiograph of airplane engine showing position of studs in crankcase.

Examination of airplane wing structure was one of many important wartime uses of X-ray.

Counter chronograph translated electric time measurements into speed of projectile flight and displayed the information on the indicator board.

High-speed differential analyzer developed by G.E. provided quick solutions of complex mathematical problems.

changed the numbers on the frames, and sent them back to the exposure position.

CHECKING POWDER IN FUSES

Throughout the war, General Electric served as a kind of clearinghouse for technical problems of both the Army and the Navy—a sort of Mayo clinic that was expected to effect a rapid diagnosis and cure. One example of this clinical performance concerned the hand grenade. The Army discovered that some of its grenades were exploding prematurely. Up to that time grenades had been tested by exploding samples selected at random. If one went off too soon, the whole lot was discarded. If the samples behaved properly, the whole lot was accepted. A more accurate test was needed to check with certainty the amount of powder in each fuse before it left the factory.

Various laboratories had been commissioned to develop such equipment, but a year went by without a satisfactory answer. The Army turned to General Electric. Within 2 weeks an automatic X-ray machine had been developed to check grenade fuses at the rate of 4,000 an hour.

For checking, fuses were set upright on a movable belt. This belt passed through a machine, where the perpendicular beam of a 200,000-volt X ray penetrated upward through each fuse and cast its glow on a fluorescent screen, above which was a phototube or "electric eye." So long as the fluorescent glow remained constant, nothing happened and the fuses passed through. However, should a fuse with a light powder charge pass over the X-ray beam, the phototube detected the change in the fluorescent glow, automatically rang a bell, flashed a red light, placed a dab of red paint on the top of the fuse, and recorded the "dud" graphically on a meter chart. This four-way check made it impossible for a fuse with an improper powder charge to get by without detection.

THE 2,000,000-VOLT X-RAY

Late in 1944, a 2-million-volt design was developed in the Research Laboratory. This new type employed the same principles as the million-volt unit, but had much more power. In this way it was possible, for the first time, to radiograph steel of 12-inch thickness. With 8-inch steel it was one hundred times faster than the million-volt unit. Although it weighed 5,000 pounds, it was mobile in the sense that it could be moved easily by crane and positioned at any desired angle by push-button electric control.

By V-J Day, four installations had been made. Two were at shell-loading plants where they permitted rapid inspection of huge shells and bombs. A third was being used by a large research organization. The fourth was scheduled for a plant making forgings for jet-propulsion engines.

STUDY OF ATOMIC STRUCTURE

Industrial X-ray units, operating at less than 50,000 volts, were widely used for diffraction studies of the atomic structure of matter. When a specimen of any material is placed in an X-ray beam, each atom in the specimen scatters the rays in many directions. These rays can be recorded on a sensitized film as a diffraction pattern, which is characteristic for that particular kind of material. Diffraction studies served to identify chemical substances, indicate structural changes in materials during processing, determine causes of premature metal failures, and develop much other valuable information concerning the materials employed in war products.

SHOCK TEST FOR SHELLS

Air-conditioning and refrigeration equipment also played a part in testing war products. It provided a method that was both foolproof and speedy for certain purposes. For example, shock testing of 37-millimeter shells for possible internal defects was part of the process of manufacture. This was done by passing the shells rapidly through a series of hot and cold baths.

The manufacturer's problem was to build the necessary equipment so it would take up the least possible amount of floor space, yet tie it in with a fast-moving production line. The problem was given careful study, and a plan was worked out whereby the shell would travel on a conveyer system, going from room temperature into a cold-water bath at 40 degrees Fahrenheit, then into a hot bath at 212 degrees, back to 40 degrees, and finally into an oil bath to prevent corrosion. The shell was made of hard, armor-piercing metal, and if it had any internal stresses, strains, or defects, the shocks of the sudden temperature changes cracked it open.

General Electric refrigeration equipment was mounted under the tanks to ensure correct temperature of the various baths. The complete apparatus occupied only 676 square feet of floor space and required only the part-time services of one girl for loading and unloading.

MEASURING PROJECTILE SPEED

Consistently reliable combat performance was a characteristic of American war equipment. Guesswork played no part in its manufacture. Components as well as finished products were subjected to rigid tests. Time after time, when there was no adequate apparatus in existence to make certain necessary tests, G.E.'s General Engineering Laboratory developed a device to meet the need.

One of these was an instrument for indicating and recording the speed of projectiles shot from large guns. Prewar methods of determining projectile speed had involved a considerable amount of time-consuming calculation. What was wanted was a device that would give an immediate answer. The apparatus evolved to do this was called a "counterchronograph." It employed, as did earlier chronographs, two circular coils of wire some distance apart through which the shell passed in succession. Passage of the shell through the first coil produced an electrical impulse, which started the counter working. Passage through the second coil stopped it. Its duration was counted in terms of the number of cycles of a current supplied by a constant-frequency generator. Time intervals could be measured to $\frac{1}{100,000}$ of a second. Since the distance between the coils was known, the counter-chronograph could translate the time interval into speed of flight. This information was then displayed electrically on an indicator board and typed on a permanent record chart. The first of these instruments was put in service early in the war at Aberdeen Proving Ground. A number of others were made later for use elsewhere.

Beginning in the early days of radar the company's Engineering Laboratory developed a wide variety of high-frequency electric instruments and devices. Special wavemeters were produced to ensure the accuracy of radio air beacons operating in the microwave-frequency range. These were particularly valuable when the Air Force was operating in the Pacific and flying several missions from the same vicinity at the same time and a number of separate directional beams were in operation simultaneously. Unless these beams functioned correctly at their proper wave lengths, serious confusion was likely to result. Wide-band oscilloscopes built by the laboratory were extremely helpful for tests made during the design and manufacture of radio equipment of all kinds.

BLUEPRINTING TORPEDO BEHAVIOR

The Navy, too, came to General Electric with difficult questions. How does a torpedo behave under water? A torpedo is like a tiny submarine without a crew and is free to move in a variety of ways. Its speed, direction, and depth are theoretically fixed before it is launched. But does it actually move as expected?

Early methods of getting answers to questions about the actual behavior included such schemes as firing torpedoes through nets and determining the depth of travel by the locations of the holes in the nets, as well as photographing the wake from the air to determine the course followed. These methods told only a partial story of the performance of the torpedo. Did it "gallop" as it went along, that is, move up and down between different levels in the water? Did it roll from side to side? Did it "yaw" from right to left in a way not disclosed by its surface wake? And what about the behavior of an electric torpedo that left no wake?

These were questions that bothered the Navy. To answer them the company's Engineering Laboratory designed the world's smallest oscillograph and placed it in the head of a torpedo to make a blueprint of the projectile's behavior under water. This little device photographed on a slowly moving roll of film a continuous set of readings of a battery of recorders that indicated depth, direction, speed, roll, and various other characteristics. After a torpedo had completed a trial run, it was removed from the water and opened up. There in the oscillograph was a complete chart showing every movement the projectile had made during the course of its travel.

TESTS FOR EVERY PURPOSE

War production demanded the most efficient possible packaging of small equipment and parts. So the laboratory designed an instrument called the "puncture tester" for evaluating the strength of packaging materials. A thickness gauge was designed to measure the thickness of electroplating, paint or lacquer films, or any other nonmagnetic film deposited on steel.

The enormous quantities of magnet wire used in war equipment created a demand for speedy and efficient wire testing. Apparatus was developed to test this wire continuously as it came off the machine instead of cutting off samples periodically for testing. A new surge test was devised for airplane magnetos to replace the old continuous-current test. Studies were made of the chemicals used in the manufacture of insulating varnishes to discover those best suited to prevent fungus growth and at the same time to withstand baking at high temperatures during the process of manufacturing electric equipment.

A wide variety of devices was produced for analyzing gases. Special gauges were developed for measuring the thickness of materials. Of particular interest was a crane-stability gauge for giving warning when the load limit of a large crane had been reached and any further loading would threaten to topple it over. They proved their worth many times on the Navy's great floating dry docks.

Heat-measuring instruments were developed to record temperatures in turbosuperchargers at high altitudes. Turbine wheels of these devices revolve at terrific speed under the impact of the engine's exhaust gases, and it is important that the critical temperature of the metal should not be exceeded. To determine actual operating temperatures, the Engineering Laboratory designed a special thermocouple actuated by heat induction without contact with the wheel itself. Other thermocouples were designed to measure the temperature of exhaust gases in jet engines.

One of the most remarkable instruments developed by the laboratory was a high-speed differential analyzer for the graphical solution of differential equations. This new type of calculator gave speedy and accurate solutions of highly complex mathematical problems that arose during the war.

Along with the development of these gauges, meters, and instruments, the laboratory built up an extensive service for the repair of instruments. This service started as a means of repairing instruments originally developed by the Engineering Laboratory when something was required beyond the simple replacement of a broken part, which could be handled by one of the company's regular service shops or the works where the instrument was produced. Under the stress of war production the laboratory's instrument service was called upon for a tremendously increased volume of repair work, handling at the peak more than 15,000 instruments a year.

Throughout the war the activities of the Engineering Laboratory in the development, production, and maintenance of testing and measuring devices continued at record-breaking levels. "Measuring instruments," as Everett S. Lee, engineer in charge of the laboratory, pointed out, "as well as shells and guns, are essential war equipment."

20

Atomic Research and Engineering

SUCCESSFUL DEVELOPMENT of the atomic bomb, which astounded the whole world on Aug. 6, 1945, has been aptly characterized as the most remarkable achievement in the history of science. When the discovery was first made that an atom of uranium 235 could be artificially induced to burst violently into two parts, the methods of isolating this rare substance were such as to produce about 1 pound in 75,000 years. To magnify small-scale laboratory experiments of this kind into operations requiring more than 2 billion dollars' worth of plant and equipment demanded a degree of confidence and daring the like of which was never seen before in any field. Nowhere except in the United States, with its immense engineering and manufacturing facilities, could this have been done in so short a time—and in the midst of a great war. That the work was kept a complete secret for nearly 3 years makes the achievement even more amazing.

No single organization or group of persons can claim a major part of the credit for an enterprise so gigantic. Scientists, engineers, workmen, and administrators—both civilian and military—all played vital roles. Included in the undertaking were the construction and maintenance of towns, roads, and schools as well as the plant and equipment for the project itself. General Electric's contributions were two-fold: (1) that of its laboratory scientists who pioneered in originally isolating uranium 235, and (2) the development and production of new and important process equipment. The company was, in fact, one of the largest producers of this process equipment, participating to the extent of about 70 million dollars. In many respects the equipment differed from anything G.E. had previously made, and required an extraordinarily high order of technical and engineering skill. Practically every major apparatus plant of the company was put to work on the project, yet the secret was so closely guarded that fewer than one hundred of the many thousands of employees knew what was being made.

URANIUM AND ATOMIC ENERGY

It has long been known that all matter—solid, liquid, or gaseous—is composed of atoms. Until comparatively recent years it was believed that the atom was the smallest unit in nature. According to this belief, the idea of the medieval alchemists that one element could be changed into another was absurd. But science was to find out that the idea was not absurd at all. The medieval alchemists were right in believing that one element could be changed into another, though they never learned how to do it. That remained to be discovered in the years that followed the ending of the World War I.

The initial step was the discovery that the atom was not the smallest unit in nature, but was rather a complex assembly of smaller units. Essentially, it was found to consist of a small heavy nucleus with a positive electric charge surrounded by a number of still smaller units called "electrons" with negative electric charges, the whole assembly being held together by the attraction of the opposing charges.

The next step was the discovery that the positive electrical charge of the nucleus (which determines what the element

is) could be altered by bombardment with atomic particles. In 1919, Sir Ernest Rutherford shot nuclei of helium
atoms at nitrogen and changed it to oxygen and hydrogen.
Thus, the transmutation sought in vain by the alchemists of
old became an actual fact. Later several other kinds of atom-
smashing bullets were used. One of the most effective proved
to be the neutron, which has no electrical charge and can
enter the nucleus unimpeded by the charge already there.

All this was intensely interesting to the scientists but made
little impression on the general public. In the 1930's, however, the really startling discovery was made that the nucleus
of a special form of uranium known as "U235" could by
neutron bombardment be made to split into two parts, with
the release of enormous quantities of energy and also of
more neutrons. These could then split more U235 nuclei
and thus a continuing chain reaction might be started. This
provided the general pattern for the atomic bomb.

ALL-OUT EFFORT BEGUN IN 1941

The significance of these developments was clearly evident
to American scientists. After a group of them had called upon
President Roosevelt and outlined the possibilities, he appointed an Advisory Committee on Uranium to continue investigation. The crux of the problem was to find a way to
obtain a sizable quantity of U235, which was then available
only in microscopic amounts. In 1940, Professor A. O. Nier
of the University of Minnesota, as well as Dr. K. H. Kingdon
and Dr. H. C. Pollock of the General Electric Research
Laboratory, had independently succeeded in isolating tiny
amounts of U235, but the quantities were measured in hun-
dred-millionths of a gram. What was wanted was a method
of making larger amounts.

Impetus was given to the uranium committee's investigation by the report that Germany was pushing atomic research
with great vigor. Nevertheless, up to the fall of 1941, activi-

ties remained on a modest scale. By that time, however, the imminence of war between Japan and the United States had become widely recognized. Consultations were held with British scientists who had been working along similar lines. In the latter part of November the Americans reported to President Roosevelt that there was a good possibility of obtaining atomic bombs for use in the impending war and urged an all-out effort for their development. It was also recommended that the existing committee be reorganized for the enlarged activity. On the day before Pearl Harbor a decision was reached to undertake the all-out effort, and the work was placed under the jurisdiction of the Office of Scientific Research and Development.

It was the splitting of the atom of U235 that led the scientists to believe that an atomic bomb could be produced. Later it was found that the artificial element plutonium (Pu 239) would react in the same way. Previous experimentation had suggested a promising method of producing plutonium.

Four different methods were known for separating U235 from natural uranium in which it exists only to the extent of one part in 140. The scientists refused to prophesy whether one of these four methods or the production of plutonium would prove to be best for the purpose of the atomic bomb, but considered that all of them were worth trying.

All four of the proposed methods of uranium separation depended on the fact that the atom of U235 was slightly lighter than the atom of natural uranium (U238). One method, that of gaseous diffusion, was based on the principle that two gases of different atomic weight can be separated by allowing some of the mixture to diffuse through a porous barrier into an evacuated space, into which the lighter passes more quickly. Another method, that of thermal diffusion, was based on the fact that separation of mixed gases can be effected by passage through a chamber having a cold region and a hot region. A third method of separation was based on centrifugal action for collecting the heavier gas at the outside of a revolving cylinder. The fourth, or electromagnetic method, separated the gases by first accelerating the atoms by an electric field and then causing them to move in a semicircular path by the influence of a powerful electromagnet. Under these conditions the lighter atoms move in smaller semicircles and can be gathered into a collector placed in the proper position.

MANHATTAN DISTRICT PROJECT

Since all four of the proposed methods for producing U235 appeared to competent scientists to hold promise of successful results, it seemed likely that the enemy's research would eventually produce successful results by one or another of them. It was deemed best therefore to proceed immediately with as much of the entire program as could be undertaken without disrupting other war activity. For this purpose in the summer of 1942 there was established the "Manhattan District" of the Corps of Engineers, United States Army, so called to conform with the usual nomenclature of the Corps' engineer districts and thus attract no special attention. The work with which it was to concern itself was labeled, for security reasons, the "DSM Project" (Development of Substitute Materials).

At this time the electromagnetic process was the only one of the four proposed processes that had actually produced U235. Although the amount was only a few milligrams isolated in a laboratory, there was no question of the scientific feasibility of the method for minute amounts. The questions were of time and cost for volume production. An enormous amount of highly complicated apparatus would have to be developed and constructed to obtain volume production. Nevertheless, on the basis of experiments at the University of California Radiation Laboratory, it looked hopeful, and in September, 1942, the OSRD recommended that an electro-magnetic separation plant be built as quickly as possible at a site previously selected at Oak Ridge in the Tennessee Valley. Originally it was planned that a pilot plant be built first, but the pressure of time was too great. Within a few weeks the building of a full-scale production plant was authorized by Brig. Gen. L. R. Groves, in charge of the Manhattan District Project.

The amount of work involved in the construction of this plant was almost incredible. A laboratory process had to be transformed into a production process on a scale many thousands of times greater. Three principal types of special process equipment were required: (1) electric power-supply apparatus and controls, (2) magnets, and (3) mechanical equipment such as receivers, pumps, tanks, etc. A careful study made by the War Department indicated that progress would be most rapid if one manufacturer concentrated on each of the three principal types of equipment. General Electric was then asked to develop and produce the power-supply apparatus and controls.

The electric equipment furnished by the company included everything from the 154,000-volt power-supply line of the Tennessee Valley Authority down through unit substations and switchgear to the individual rectifiers. Unit substations were provided with automatic voltage regulation, a particularly important factor where electronic devices are used.

Most of the power for this plant flowed through electronic tubes, of which the company supplied many thousands of various sizes. A complete new factory was constructed at East Hampton, Mass., for manufacturing these tubes. The speed at which the job had to be handled is indicated by the fact that in the early stages the company was producing the equipment at a rate of one million dollars a week.

In connection with this project a group of G-E scientists

and engineers numbering as many as fifteen at times, was stationed for nearly 3 years at the University of California Radiation Laboratory where continuing experiments were being made. A second group, averaging more than twenty members, was stationed at Oak Ridge.

The first section of the electromagnetic separation plant was ready for operation in November, 1943. By the latter part of 1944, the plant was in large-scale operation and producing U235 of sufficient purity for use in atomic bombs.

GASEOUS-DIFFUSION PLANT

At the same time that work was started on the electromagnetic separation plant, plans were being drawn up for a second plant at Oak Ridge to utilize the gaseous-diffusion method. It was proposed to obtain U235 by converting natural uranium into a gas and make use of the difference in velocity of U235 and U238 in diffusing through a porous barrier. Uranium being a solid metal, the first problem was to transform it into a gas. This involved the selection of a compound of uranium that would be gaseous at workable temperatures, and from which the U235 could be readily regained after diffusion. Fluorine was considered most suitable for compounding because it would not complicate the process by adding any undesired combinations. Its use introduced serious complications, however, because of its being extremely corrosive and poisonous.

It was evident from the start that a large number of diffusion stages would be required. Estimates were made that several thousand would be necessary. It was evident also that at least several hundred stages would be necessary for "stripping." This meant a plant sprawling over a huge area with enormous pumping and cooling requirements. As actually built, the plant totaled some 70 buildings distributed over 600 acres. Vast quantities of air-conditioning equipment were needed to prevent moisture and dust from getting into the system and also to give the workers protection against poisonous fumes.

About half the total power required was steam generated and half purchased from the Tennessee Valley Authority. General Electric Company supplied turbine-generators having a combined capacity equivalent to that of an enormous central power station. The company also supplied all the outdoor high-voltage substation equipment, and many of the auxiliary motors, switchgear, much other apparatus, and a million dollars worth of electric cable for the powerhouse, the material-conditioning plant, and the process plant.

G.E.'s General Engineering Laboratory did the development and production for the multimillion-dollar instrumentation program. It produced the finished designs and arranged for production both within the company and with scores of outside subcontractors. Probably the most important part of this instrumentation was for gas analysis where extremely complex electrical methods were required. Hundreds of mass spectrometers were made for this purpose as well as for leak detection. Other instruments included flow-meters, pressure meters, etc. By these means it was possible to monitor the flow of gases at all times and quickly to spot the exact location of any leak.

Construction of the power station, the first unit to be built for the gaseous-diffusion plant, was started in June, 1943. Other units were started later that year. By the early part of 1945, the entire plant had been completed and was in successful operation.

It was not until the summer of 1944 that construction was started on the thermal-diffusion plant. Experiments at the Naval Research Laboratory had early indicated the theoretical feasibility of producing U235 by the thermal-diffusion method, but this method had the practical drawback of requiring enormous quantities of steam. A special combination of circumstances, however, made it feasible to proceed with the construction of a thermal plant. One consideration was that a large amount of steam could be quite easily obtained from the power station built for the gaseous-diffusion plant. Another consideration was that the output of the electromagnetic plant could be substantially increased by enriching the material with which it was fed. For example, an electromagnetic unit that could produce a gram a day of 40 per cent pure U235 from natural uranium could produce 2 grams a day of 80 per cent U235 if the concentration of U235 in the feed material was sufficiently increased. Under these circumstances it was decided to proceed with the construction of a thermal-diffusion plant at Oak Ridge.

General Electric's contribution to this project comprised standard electric apparatus and a large amount of instrumentation. Construction of the plant was completed in the space of a few months. Its operation accomplished the intended purpose of increasing the production rate of the electromagnetic plant, though difficulties were experienced in obtaining sufficient steam when the gaseous-diffusion plant was in full operation.

A pilot plant was built to utilize the centrifuge method of separation, but the engineering difficulties appeared to be too great to warrant the building of a production plant.

Hardly less remarkable than the development of these huge electrical and chemical plants was the creation of the "hidden" city of Oak Ridge. There have been other "hidden" cities in the world's history but never one that grew so swiftly. The site, 18 miles west of Knoxville, was acquired in the autumn of 1942. It was chosen because of its accessibility to electric power and water, its distance from the seaboard, and its isolation.

The first family moved into a trailer home in July, 1943. By the spring of 1945, Oak Ridge had a population of 78,000. At the height of its construction, a thousand houses a month were being built.

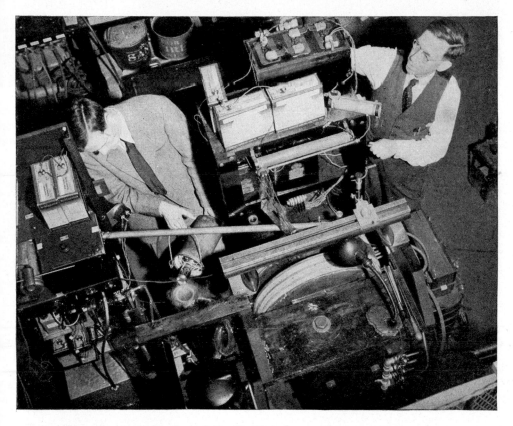

Drs. H. C. Pollock and K. H. Kingdon with mass spectrometer used in isolating U-235 in G.E. Research Laboratory in 1940.

Part of the plant at Oak Ridge for electro-magnetic separation of U-235.

Outdoor electric equipment for electro-magnetic separation process.

Administration Building housing the offices of the vast and complex Manhattan Engineer District at Oak Ridge.

Main business center at Oak Ridge where stores, theatres, a bank, the town hall and other enterprises were located.

Main structure of the gaseous diffusion plant at Oak Ridge.

Cooling towers which handled the enormous volume of water required for the gaseous diffusion process.

Largest steam plant ever constructed in one operation supplied 238,000 kilowatts of power and process steam for operation at Oak Ridge.

Side view of gigantic plant for gaseous diffusion.

Mass spectrometer for measuring U-235 concentration.

*An elementary school and group of workers'
homes at Oak Ridge.*

*Richland, the home and business area for the
Hanford Engineer Works.*

*One of the seven production areas at the Hanford
Engineer Works.*

Another large production area at Hanford.

Along with the houses the construction job involved the building of nine elementary schools, one high school, three churches, thirteen supermarkets, nine drugstores, seven theaters, seventeen restaurants and lunch rooms, a library, and a hospital. More than 300 miles of road were built or improved in the area, a substantial part of the street lighting being furnished by General Electric. Simultaneously with the road construction was the building of sewers, water works, and other municipal services. Thus, in less than 3 years, Oak Ridge grew from nothing to be the fifth largest city in the state of Tennessee.

HANFORD ENGINEER WORKS

In addition to the plants for the production of U235 at Oak Ridge, the Manhattan District Project included the construction of a huge plant on the Columbia River near Pasco, Wash., for the production of plutonium. This plant was known as the "Hanford Engineer Works."

During the course of experiments at the University of Chicago Metallurgical Laboratory, it had been discovered that the atom of plutonium could be split in the same way as the atom of U235 and that the process would result similarly in the release of enormous quantities of energy. Thus plutonium could be used in an atomic bomb in the same way as uranium 235. Moreover, the prospect seemed brighter of producing and separating sizable quantities of the artificial element plutonium (Pu 239), since the process required only the addition of a neutron to each atom of U238, the form in which uranium was found quite abundantly in nature.

A pilot plant for producing plutonium was first built at Oak Ridge. It was soon realized, however, that this site was not satisfactory for large-scale production. Power requirements for the operation of such a plant would be greater than the supply available in the Tennessee Valley after the demands of the other plants of the Manhattan District Project had been met. Moreover, it was believed remotely possible that the plutonium production process might spread radioactive material over a wide area. For these reasons an isolated site was selected on the Columbia River not far away from the huge hydroelectric power plant at Grand Coulee Dam. General Electric's contribution to this project was principally in the form of large quantities of standard electric apparatus such as motors for driving water pumps, etc. By the early summer of 1945 this plant was in operation and producing plutonium.

USE OF ATOMIC BOMBS

Assembly of the first atomic bomb began on the night of July 12, 1945, at an old ranch house on the desert at Los Alamos, N.M., about 20 miles from Santa Fe. This location had been selected for reasons of secrecy and safety. An extraordinary galaxy of scientists was on hand from all over the country. Tension ran high. All realized that the moment was approaching when they might find themselves at the threshold of a new era of science or when they might be blasted into eternity.

At the end of 2 days' preparation the bomb was hoisted to the top of a remote 100-foot steel tower. Another day was spent in final arrangements. Then the scientists withdrew to a distance of about 6 miles to watch what happened. At 5:30 A.M. on July 16 a blinding flash, brighter than the brightest sunlight, lighted up the whole area. It was followed by a deafening roar, and a huge cloud of multicolored smoke billowed high up into the air.

The experiment had worked. The bomb had exploded as intended. The steel tower had completely disappeared. Where it had stood there was only a tremendous crater. The whole performance had followed closely the predictions of science.

The first target of America's new weapon was Hiroshima,

an important military center and port of embarkation for Japanese troops. An atomic bomb having more power than 20,000 tons of TNT was dropped there on August 6 with devastating effect. Three days later another atomic bomb was dropped on Nagasaki. History, alone, can evaluate exactly the importance of the military results accomplished. Aside from the direct effect of great damage to important Japanese military and naval installations, they undoubtedly had a potent influence in hastening Japan's surrender in the latter part of the same month.

Even if nothing more had been accomplished, the expenditure of 2 billion dollars would appear to have been fully justified. Actually, a good deal more was accomplished than can be measured in terms of the effect upon Japan. In the first place, the project was a vitally important safeguard against the possibility that German research might develop an atomic bomb that would enable her to win the war after her armed forces had been forced to the threshold of surrender. In the second place, the knowledge gained during the progress of the project opened the door to future use of atomic power in a world at peace.

FUTURE OF ATOMIC POWER

As soon as the censorship which had cloaked the development of the atomic bomb was lifted, predictions were freely made that atomic power would quickly revolutionize the way of living of the whole world. Scientists who had worked on the project were more cautious. While it was known that the energy released from the breaking up of a pound of such material as uranium or plutonium was equivalent to that obtained from burning 1,500 tons of coal, the engineering problems involved in harnessing this energy remained to be solved. As Dr. C. G. Suits, director of G.E.'s Research Laboratory pointed out, the development of economical atomic power could not be expected to come about as a simple by-product from the atomic bomb. Much of the knowledge gained from the bomb project promised to have application to the problem of atomic-power production, but a great deal of research was needed before practical use could be made of it.

In the summer of 1946, the War Department announced the transfer to General Electric of the responsibility for operation of the Hanford Engineer Works and the inauguration of an extensive program for atomic energy research and development. The contract specified that the fee for all the work performed was to be one dollar a year.

Commenting on the company's new responsibility, President Charles E. Wilson said,

"General Electric was engaged in atomic research for peacetime application before the war. With this background we are convinced that the quickest possible development of nonmilitary applications is the most constructive solution to the problem which atomic energy presents to the world."

APPENDIX A

Mobilizing Machines and Men

UNDER THE GRIM URGENCY of war the General Electric Company crowded 12 years' production into 4 years. Each new job that was undertaken created need for greater plant capacity and more personnel. But buildings and equipment and workers do not materialize by rubbing Aladdin's lamp. They arise out of the forethought, planning, and hard work of men who accept the task of achieving the impossible.

One day word came from the Electronics Department to J. M. Howell, works manager at Schenectady, that the Army and Navy were likely to double their demands for radar equipment at any moment, and that additional manufacturing space would soon be urgently needed.

"All right," he answered calmly, "we'll look around and find space somewhere."

Not a square foot of space was available in existing buildings, but it might be possible for the company to arrange for the use of a neighboring plant and 24 acres of ground belonging to a former manufacturer of wiring supplies. So Howell called the engineer in charge of real estate who drove 60 miles back to Schenectady that afternoon. After dinner the engineer, Howell, and E. D. Spicer, vice-president in charge of manufacturing, inspected the property. There they found that about 60,000 square feet of old factory space could be reclaimed without much trouble and that plenty of room was available on the property to erect a new 250,000 square foot plant.

The general idea was approved by the Defense Coordinating Committee. Vice-president W. R. G. Baker, head of the Electronics Department, reported the situation to President Charles E. Wilson in New York, who called Secretary of the Navy Knox and Rear Admiral Robinson of the Bureau of Ships. All agreed to the plan. Company representatives proceeded to Washington and within 2 weeks the owner of the factory signed a contract with the Defense Plant Corporation. A couple of days later the old building was being cleaned up and the construction of a new plant was being planned. Scarcity of materials delayed it, wood trusses instead of steel had to be used for the roof, but a fully equipped factory was in operation inside of 4 months.

Before the war General Electric had 34 plants with 29 million feet of floor space. Besides the huge Schenectady Works, additional large plants were in operation at Bloomfield, N.J., Bridgeport, Conn., Cleveland, Ohio., Decatur, Ind., Erie, Pa., Fort Wayne, Ind., Philadelphia, Pa., Pittsfield, Mass., Oakland, Calif., and West Lynn, Mass. Smaller plants were in operation in numerous other places.

Between 1940 and Sept. 1, 1945, eleven major new plants were put in operation. These were located at Buffalo, N.Y., Darby, Pa., East Hampton, Mass., Syracuse, N.Y., Everett, Mass., Fitchburg, Mass., Fort Edward, N.Y., Kokomo, Ind., Lowell, Mass., Cleveland, Ohio, and Trenton, N.J. Besides the new plants, large additions were made to existing facilities at Bloomfield, Decatur, Erie, Fort Wayne, Oakland, Philadelphia, Pittsfield, Schenectady, and West Lynn. By the end of the war the company had a total of sixty-eight plants with 41 million square feet of floor space.

BUILDING AT TOP SPEED

Speed was the keynote throughout the expansion program. Providing additional facilities for turbine manufacture at Erie was typical. On June 10, 1941, the company received word that the Maritime Commission needed propulsion equipment for a hundred C-3 cargo ships and wanted it quickly. As existing facilities for making turbines and gears were already overcrowded, it was obvious that additional plant capacity would have to be provided. The War Projects Committee decided to build the additional turbines at Erie. On June 18, the company submitted cost estimates. On July 9, a lease was signed with the Defense Plant Corporation and ground was broken for a new 8-acre plant adjacent to the existing plant there.

Construction gangs worked 24 hours a day, using flood-lights at night, throughout the fall and early winter to drain and clear the ground. A brook traversing the area had to be diverted before the concrete foundations were poured. To bring the new plant into production more quickly, the con-crete flooring and the foundations for the machine tools were laid before the erection of steel. Steel work was begun on November 7. By December 7, the entire 2,800 tons of steel for the framework had been erected.

For the manufacturing program nearly 300 machine tools were required, ranging in size from small milling machines and drill presses to huge 16-foot vertical boring mills weigh-ing 110 tons. They were obtained from nearly a hundred different suppliers. Forty manufacturers supplied jigs and fixtures alone.

As soon as part of the building was sided and roofed, the machine tools were installed. Although much of the struc-ture was still open, production started immediately, the workers being protected from the weather by tarpaulins and kept warm by salamanders. The building was formally occupied on Feb. 12, 1942.

The original production schedule called for the delivery of the first shaft, consisting of a high-pressure and a low-pressure turbine, by Aug. 1, 1942. As a result of the quick construction of the building, however, and the speed achieved in manufacturing, the first unit was actually completed more than 2 months ahead of schedule.

The company's wartime expansion program was financed in two ways. General Electric in most cases paid the cost of new buildings when they were erected on land owned and retained by the company. Elsewhere, construction and alteration costs were paid by the Defense Plant Corporation and the properties leased to the company. The existing structures taken over and used for war work included old warehouses, automobile salesrooms, garages—and even an old armory. At Syracuse a street-car repair shop was converted into a factory for making radar equipment. In Kokomo a glass factory was taken over for making generators and small motors.

Altogether, from the beginning of 1940 to the end of the war, General Electric invested 155 million dollars of its own money in additional war-production facilities. During the same period the Defense Plant Corporation and other government agencies spent a total of 158 million dollars for buildings and equipment leased to the company.

RECRUITING ADDITIONAL WORKERS

Before the war General Electric employed about 76,000 workers; at the end of the war the number was approximately 170,000. But that does not tell the whole story. While the company was increasing its working force by some 94,000, it had to find replacements for about 50,000 employees who entered the armed forces and many thousand of others whose services were lost through death, retirement, or other causes. Altogether more than 200,000 men and women were recruited, trained, and put to work during the period of war activity.

Some of the new employees were part-time workers. Men and women who worked in the company's offices during the daytime went into the shops and put in a short shift of extra work in the evening. Lawyers, real-estate agents, insurance salesmen, clerks in stores, and many others did factory work after hours. When the afternoon dismissal bell rang in Schenectady schools, many teachers and students hurried down to punch the time clock at the G.E. Works. At least one minister of a near-by church worked the night shift at one plant, taking Saturday as his night off each week so that he would be fresh to preach to his congregation on Sunday.

As the war continued, women went to work in increasing numbers, not only in the offices, but in the factories as well. Former music teachers, ex-newspaper writers, a retired head-waitress, a minister's wife, numerous grandmothers, and hundreds of housewives helped produce weapons of war at the company's plants throughout the country. Some former beauty-shop workers found that dexterity developed in curling hair was valuable training for delicate assembly operations. Hundreds of women were trained for drafting work. Numerous college girls, mostly graduates in mathematics and physics, were assigned to engineering work. Some women drove trucks. Others became machine-tool operators. In 1940, women numbered 20 per cent of the company's employees; in 1944 they constituted 40 per cent.

Reasons that prompted the women to go into war work were many and various. Four were listed by one young woman who worked on an assembly line. Her husband was serving in the United States Navy. Her father, a former employee at Schenectady, had gone back to his native Holland and had been interned in a German hostage camp. Two of her brothers, living in Holland, had been drafted by the Germans as slave laborers in Nazi factories. She couldn't do less, she thought, than undertake a war-production job in America.

A gray-haired woman who ran a lathe at the Pittsfield Works said, "I've decided that my place is at a machine where I can do something to help. I worked in a machine shop in the last war. My son is missing in action somewhere in the Pacific, and I'd do anything to help now."

HOUSING SHORTAGES

Finding a place to live was difficult everywhere during the war. Long before manufacturing activity reached its peak all existing housing facilities were crowded in the cities where the company's plants were located, and still the demand grew for more and more workers. Some of those who came to work solved the housing problem by living a long distance away and making a lengthy trip back and forth each day. A woman tractor driver at the Pittsfield Works commuted daily by automobile to her home 30 miles away at North Pownal, Vt. One winter Sunday her house burned to the ground, but she reported for work next morning at eight o'clock, just the same as usual, though the temperature that day was 40 degrees below zero.

Back in 1937, when the locomotive business was booming, the company's plant at Erie employed 6,500 workers. By 1941, when the plant was busy making 75-millimeter howitzers for the Army and turbines for the Navy, the number had risen to 10,000, and new workers were being taken on at a rate of 150 a week. Construction of a 500-home "Defense Village" had been started by the government, but something had to be done to meet the pressing need that arose before the project could be completed.

So the government established a trailer camp. Some 250 trailers were wheeled in and parked right in the shadow of the factory's tall chimney. Laundry and lavatory facilities were provided in centralized utility buildings. Trailers rented for $6 a week. A large playground for the children was equipped with slides and swings. Grocers, butchers, and milkmen made regular deliveries in the camp, but "bell ringers" were forbidden so that night-shift workers could sleep undisturbed during the day.

TRAINING NEW EMPLOYEES

Training the company's 200,000 new wartime employees was no simple undertaking. It requires months to make a passable soldier, but it takes even longer to make a good mechanic. To train its new workers and retrain older employees, the company set up a program of instruction in which workers were taught quickly to perform certain specific jobs. While this type of training did not produce all-around mechanics, it proved to be an excellent solution of the war emergency problem.

Somewhat similar training courses were conducted for women. As most of them worked on light assembly lines, however, it was usually possible to make these courses shorter than those for machine operators. In the case of personnel hired for new factories, women were frequently trained while the plant was being built. In one instance a near-by garage was converted to a training school. Thus, the workers were ready to start as soon as the new structure was completed. Altogether the cost of training the company's new wartime worker, was over 80 million dollars.

DIVIDING THE PRODUCTION LOAD

Even before Pearl Harbor, General Electric had been hard pressed to meet the production demands of the National Defense Program, and the company had turned to smaller manufacturers throughout the country to do certain parts of the job. The work done by these subcontractors included designing and making tools, dies, jigs, and fixtures; making screw-machine parts, metal stampings, wood and metal patterns, forgings, castings, and gears of all sizes and types. Miscellaneous machine work was "farmed out," too—shaft turning, boring, planing, broaching, milling, grinding, drilling and tapping; electroplating; medium and heavy sheet-metal fabricating; and subassembly work.

Manufacture of the powerful 60-inch searchlight, for which General Electric had over-all responsibility represented the combined efforts of a score of firms. Its steel reflector was ground and polished by companies in New Jersey, Virginia, and Ohio. Its front-door glass was made by concerns in Pennsylvania and Michigan. Arc carbons came from Ohio and arc switches from Michigan. Parts of the steel base were made by a firm in New York and its aluminum castings came from still another firm in Ohio.

At one time G.E. was employing the services of more than 2,000 subcontractors. They supplied equipment ranging in size from tiny taper pins weighing less than an ounce to huge castings weighing 40 tons. The facilities of a gravestone maker were enlisted to sandblast castings for electrical apparatus. A manufacturer of mattress-tying machinery made parts for turbines.

After a search of several weeks among established metalworking concerns for a subcontractor to produce a special machine part needed in large quantities by the Philadelphia Works, the answer was finally discovered in a manufacturer of fishing tackle. A burial-casket company was found to be well equipped to make steel cabinets for radio equipment.

Extra-fine precision work was turned out by a small plant formerly engaged in the manufacture of model airplane engines. This firm, which employed only ten highly skilled workmen, specialized for years in making tiny gasoline motors weighing a mere 21 ounces, yet capable of generating ¾ horsepower. When the national emergency arose, they were anxious to play a part, so the manager went to General Electric and asked to be allowed to try some precision work.

He was given a trial order, and from the first his company produced extremely accurate and high-class work—work on which a number of large machining firms had previously failed to attain the accuracy required.

Besides the instances where General Electric remained the prime contractor when it sublet part of the work to others, there were numerous instances where the company turned over its designs and drawings to other concerns that were additional prime contractors or subcontractors on the same product.

At a stockholders' meeting at Schenectady on April 21, 1942, President Wilson pointed out that:

Men who go to war give not only their time and money to their country, but some part of themselves. In this emergency corporations can do no less. We have freely given to others, many of them our competitors, so that the production job might be enlarged and speeded, our designs, our patents and our experience, the only things we have to give in addition to our own efforts. Before Pearl Harbor, we agreed to make available any of our designs and techniques that may be required by the Army or the Navy, for manufacturing by others, whether patented or unpatented. I repeat that offer again now, for the record, to hold good for the duration of the war.

Assistance of this sort was given on turbines for ship propulsion; generators, motors, and controls for submarines; switchgear, controls, and cable for naval ships; motors, generators, amplidynes, and superchargers for airplanes; searchlights and radio for the Army and Navy; and numerous other items.

STANDARDIZATION OF DESIGN

Maximum conservation of time and materials was vital to the war-production job. A program of repetitive manufacture of certain standardized designs was followed wherever possible. This was done even with such heavy apparatus as propulsion equipment for the Navy and the Merchant Marine.

"We built a shining new plant somewhere west of the Alleghenies (actually at Erie) to produce 30,000-horsepower ship-propulsion turbines," commented Vice-president Lang in the summer of 1942. "We whistled bravely, knocked on wood, and kept our fingers crossed because at another plant where we've always built large turbines—practically no two of them alike—we have never averaged more than a third so many units of comparable size per month. Are we going to meet the seemingly blue-sky schedule? No we're going to exceed it by producing at least two-thirds again as many— thanks to duplicated manufacture of standardized design." In fact, the schedule was exceeded by an amount even larger than Mr. Lang predicted.

Repetitive manufacture speeded the production of a great variety of other equipment of a less complicated nature than turbines. What could be done in this direction, however, was limited by the necessity to make numerous changes in design as the war progressed.

"Throughout the war," according to General Eisenhower, "there was a noticeable and steady improvement in many of our weapons and equipment. Such improvement is mandatory always; the alternative is stagnation and eventual disaster."

Changes in the design of electric generators for aircraft furnish a characteristic example of benefitting by combat experience. At the start of the war a standard type of aircraft generator was in production in large volume. Then came Jimmy Doolittle's spectacular raid on Tokyo. As the distances involved in the flight were exceptionally long for those days, a considerable amount of the flying was done at cruising speed to conserve gasoline. The electric generators, however, were designed for operation on shorter flights with the planes' engines running at higher speeds, and they failed to supply the intended amount of current. By the time the fliers reached Tokyo the batteries had become so weak from insufficient charging that the whole electrical system was functioning erratically, and the crews had to kick the bomb-bay doors open. This showed plainly the need for modification of the plane's power-generating system. Redesign was undertaken immediately so that ample power would be available at all times regardless of flying speed.

Throughout the whole period of the war the design of antiaircraft gun directors on shipboard and on land was undergoing constant change to meet the increasing speed of the enemy's planes. Eventually it even became necessary for the gun directors to match the speed of the "buzz bombs." So the apparatus was modified again to meet the new conditions. Designs of virtually every sort of equipment at the end of the war were very different from the early designs.

CONSERVATION OF MATERIALS

War production demanded previously unheard-of quantities of materials of almost every kind. Available supplies were insufficient to meet all these needs. Among the scarce materials were such metals as steel, aluminum, chromium, copper, magnesium, nickel, tin, and tungsten. This scarcity necessitated changes in the design of many of the products made by General Electric.

Conservation of critical materials was effected in some instances by a straight substitution of something else in place of the standard material without any significant change in design. For example, 175 tons of aluminum, urgently needed for aircraft, were saved annually by substituting other materials for name plates on apparatus manufactured by the company.

More often conservation involved a reduction in the amount of material used for a particular purpose. For each type of apparatus using critical materials, a design was worked out from the standpoint of material scarcity rather than from the standpoint of ease and economy of manufacture. A technique of cutting "jigsaw puzzles" was developed whereby parts to be cut from flat sections—circles, semicircles, triangles, squares, stars, and many other shapes— were so carefully laid out and nested together that hardly any surplus metal remained as scrap after the cutting had been done.

A third class of conservation involved the use of an alternate material accompanied by a change of design. An outstanding example of this was the change from aluminum to steel construction in many instances. Usually this required a complete redesigning job as well as changes in manufacturing methods and equipment.

Important economies in the use of critical materials were made by all these methods. Considering aluminum alone, huge savings were obtained in addition to that accomplished by the change of name plates. These others included 650 tons a year in meter production, 275 tons in industrial control gear, 180 tons in street-lighting equipment, 100 tons in lightning-protective devices, and about 80 tons in switchgear construction. More than 200 tons of tin were saved yearly by reducing the tin content of certain solders.

Supplementing efforts to conserve critical materials was a far-reaching salvage program. By salvaging everything not actually used or useful the company recovered 380 million pounds of scrap material in a single year—enough to fill every car in a hundred full-length freight trains. At one plant some 2,500 obsolete rubber stamps were turned in. At another location an old power plant, no longer in operation, yielded 27 carloads of scrap when dismantled. A third plant collected several carloads of obsolete dies and tools, some dating back more than 50 years to the time of Frank Sprague's early electrical experiments.

BIRTH OF A GREAT NEW WARRIOR

In these and many other ways the change-over from peacetime to wartime production presented a host of difficult problems. But, everywhere they were tackled with energy and enthusiasm. The prevailing spirit was shown at the Erie Works when a celebration was held to say good-bye to the last peacetime refrigerator to travel down the production line. The spirit of the occasion was expressed in a message fancifully directed to the Axis powers.

Most of us here at the ceremony have been making electric refrigerators for nearly a generation. You might say that it's been almost our life's work—and we've enjoyed it immensely. Problems? Sure, we had many problems. We had to master engineering and manufacturing problems. Down through the years, we've been putting our heads together constantly with but one objective—to make the most perfect refrigerator we could for the least money. And why? Just so cab drivers and coal miners, school teachers and store clerks, and folks like them could own one.

Now you might think that this, then, was a sad day—if something like a refrigerator meant so much to us. But, be not deceived! There is no sadness. Rather, a fierce, burning joy. It wasn't a burial, no it was a birth. The birth of a Great New Warrior who will join with other Great Strong Warriors reborn since December 7. And these Great Strong Warriors are on the march already.

You thought our President was kidding, didn't you, when he mentioned our Production Program; when he gave you all those enormous figures for guns and tanks and ships and planes. He wasn't kidding. They're on the way now. And coming so fast the quotas will be doubled if need be.

How is it possible? Well, free men are making them—men who want to make guns and planes and tanks and ships. Millions of free men working without bayonets at their backs. Working longer hours, getting along with less comforts, and not complaining. Free men singing a free song, working for freedom.

G-E Plants and Principal War Products

All the products shown in this list were manufactured for war purposes. Though some are similar in name to ordinary commercial products, the great majority were new in design, and in every instance they were produced for the use of the Armed Forces, the Merchant Marine, or essential war industries.

PLANT LOCATION	PRINCIPAL PRODUCTS
Andover, Ohio	Ampoules for V-T fuses (*L*)
Bellevue, Ohio	Photoflash lamps for aerial photography (*L*)
Bloomfield, N.J.	Components for Navy torpedoes
	Components for remote-control turret systems, heating and air-conditioning equipment, searchlights, heat-transfer coolers for rectifiers, transformers, etc. (*AC*)
	Components for remote-control turret systems, control devices (*A*)
Bridgeport, Conn.	Airplane magneto-ignition harness, airplane starting and warming cable, artillery rocket launchers, ba-

NOTE—Letters in parentheses following list of products indicate department responsible: *A* = Apparatus, *AC* = Air Conditioning, *AM* = Appliance and Merchandising, *C* = Chemical, *E* = Electronics, *L* = Lamp.

PLANT LOCATION	PRINCIPAL PRODUCTS
	zooka rocket launchers, dynamotors, electric ship fittings, electric torpedoes, electrically heated flying suits, height finder covers, servo gyro covers; gun chargers, high-frequency cable, junction boxes and circuit breakers for tanks, Navy cable, proportional bank adapters, remote-control turret equipment, searchlights, shipboard fans, tinsel cord for tanks and aircraft, twisted field wire, underwater listening devices (*AM*)
	Radar equipment, radio-communication equipment (*E*)
Bridgeville, Pa.	Glass bulbs and tubing (*L*)
Bucyrus, Ohio	Fluorescent lamps (*L*)
Buffalo, N.Y.	Electronic tubes (*L*)
Cleveland, Ohio	Bulbs for lamps and radio tubes, chemicals, fluorescent lamps and tubing, incandescent lamps, lamp bases, lead-in wires for lamps and radio tubes, quartz products, radio and cathode-ray tubes, shells, sights and computers for remote-control turrets (*L*)
Conneaut, Ohio	Lamp bases (*L*)
Danbury, Conn.	Shipboard fans (*AM*)
Darby, Pa.	Direct turret control for aircraft (*A*)
Decatur, Ind.	Fractional horsepower motors (*A*)
East Boston, Mass.	Incandescent lamps, lead-in wires for lamps and radio tubes (*L*)
East Hampton, Mass.	Electronic tubes (*E*)
Erie, Pa.	Gun mounts, 75-mm howitzers, motors, portable power plants, remote control turret assembly, ship-propulsion turbines, transportation equipment (*A*)
Euclid, Ohio	Tungsten powder, rods and wire,

PLANT LOCATION	PRINCIPAL PRODUCTS
	molybdenum rods and wire, gases (L)
Everett, Mass.	Turbosuperchargers, steel castings (A)
Fitchburg, Mass.	Navy auxiliary turbines (A)
Fort Edward, N.Y.	Selsyns for remote-control turret systems (A)
Fort Wayne, Ind.	Compressors for remote-control turret systems, recoil mechanisms for guns, refrigeration equipment, supercharger components (AC)
	Amplidynes, fractional-horsepower motors, impellers, magnet wire, magnetos, aircraft turrets, motors and generators, specialty transformers, turbosuperchargers (A)
	Molded plastics products (C)
Hoboken, N.J.	High intensity incandescent lamps (L)
Holyoke, Mass.	Plastics fuses for trench-mortar shells (C)
Jackson, Miss.	Fluorescent lamps (L)
Kokomo, Ind.	Direct-current generators (A)
Lowell, Mass.	Aircraft rocket launcher clusters, electrically heated bombsight covers, camera covers, casualty blankets, flying suits, flying gloves, flying shoes (AM)
River Works, West Lynn, Mass.	Aircraft gas turbines, arc-welding equipment, signaling searchlights, motors and generators, ship-propulsion gears, copper oxide and selenium rectifiers, turbines, turbosuperchargers (A)
	Fabroil gears, laminated rods, sheets and tubes; molded laminated plastics products, radar housings, heated goggles (C)
West Lynn Works, West Lynn, Mass.	Aircraft instruments, meters and instruments, radio-communication equipment (A)

PLANT LOCATION	PRINCIPAL PRODUCTS
	Radar equipment, radio-communications equipment (*E*)
Meriden, Conn.	Molded and fabricated plastics products (*C*)
Mount Vernon, N.Y.	Airplane starting and warming cable, headsets and cord sets for wire communication (*AM*)
Newark, N.J.	Incandescent lamps (*L*)
New Kensington, Pa.	Glider tow-rope indicator, heavy cable and conduit products, pilot's control sticks (*AM*)
New Milford, Conn.	Electrically heated bombsight covers, camera covers, and flying suits (*AM*)
Niles, Ohio	Glass bulbs (*L*)
Oakland, Calif.	Distribution transformers, motors and switchgear, wire and cable (*A*)
Ontario, Calif.	Incandescent lamps (*L*)
	Gun heaters and control for aircraft, metal assemblies for incendiary bombs, oil immersion heaters, oxygen pressure switch, parachute pack rack, temperature control for aircraft (*AM*)
Philadelphia, Pa.	Switchgear, torpedo controls (*A*)
Pittsfield, Mass.	Capacitors, distribution and power transformers, gun directors, industrial heating, motors and generators, high-voltage rectifiers (*A*)
	Chemicals, molding compounds and resins, molded plastics products (*C*)
Poughkeepsie, N.Y.	Building wire (*AM*)
Providence, R.I.	Lamp bases, metal radio-tube shells, bomb-nose fuse parts (*L*)
St. Louis, Mo.	Incandescent lamps (*L*)
Schenectady, N.Y.	Aeronautical devices, aircraft gas turbines, generators, gun-fire control, hydraulic gun control, industrial control, industrial heating,

PLANT LOCATION	PRINCIPAL PRODUCTS
	motors, searchlights, synchronous converters, turbines and turbine generators, voltage regulators, welding equipment, wire and cable (A)
	Glyptal solutions, insulation materials, silicones (C)
	Electronic tubes, radar equipment, radio-communication equipment (E)
Scranton, Pa.	Molded plastics products (C)
Syracuse, N.Y.	Aircraft gas turbines, destroyer escort turbines and generators (A)
	Radar equipment, radio-communication equipment (E)
Taunton, Mass.	Molded plastics products, mycalex (C)
Trenton, N.J.	Switchgear (A)
Warren, Ohio	Sealed Beam lamps, emergency signaling mirrors, incandescent lamps (L)
White Plains, N.Y.	Motors for aircraft turrets, Disposalls (AM)
York, Pa.	Aircraft wire, magnet wires, Navy cable, switchboard cable, toasters for Navy (AM)
Youngstown, Ohio	Incandescent lamps (L)

AFFILIATED COMPANIES

NAME	PRINCIPAL PRODUCTS
Carboloy Co., Inc., Detroit, Mich.	Carbide cores for antitank shells, cemented carbides for tools and dies

NAME	PRINCIPAL PRODUCTS
Edison General Electric Appliance Co., Chicago, Ill. (now Hotpoint, Inc.)	Ammunition boxes, antiaircraft direction finders, bombs, cartridge cases, machine-gun trainers, shell cores, shipboard electric cooking equipment
General Electric X-Ray Corp., Chicago, Ill.	Medical, dental and industrial X-ray equipment, other medical equipment, antiaircraft gun directors, manual rate-matching mechanisms, radio tubes
Locke Insulator Corp., Baltimore, Md.	Ceramic insulators and pole line hardware for radar, radio, telephone and telegraph, power distribution and transmission.
The Monowatt Electric Corp., Providence, Rhode Island	Rectifiers; wiring devices, connections and assemblies
Telechron Inc., Ashland, Mass.	Firing pins, fuses, primers, relays, speed indicators, timing devices
The Trumbull Electric Mfg. Co., Plainville, Conn.	Electrical control apparatus

APPENDIX C

Production Awards to G-E Plants

During the war the Army-Navy E was awarded to nineteen plants of the General Electric Company and its affiliates for excellence in production. The Maritime Commission M was awarded to three plants. Stars indicating continued excellence in production were awarded on fifty-four occasions, making a total of seventy-six awards.

BRIDGEPORT WORKS

Original Award	Army-Navy E	Mar. 26, 1943
Second Award	Army-Navy E	Sept. 25, 1943
Third Award	Army-Navy E	July 4, 1944
Fourth Award	Army-Navy E	Jan. 13, 1945
Fifth Award	Army-Navy E	Sept. 21, 1945

ERIE WORKS

Original Award	Navy E	Sept. 19, 1941
Second Award	Navy E	Mar. 30, 1942
Third Award	Navy E	May 30, 1942
Fourth Award	Army-Navy E	Sept. 26, 1942
Fifth Award	Army-Navy E	Mar. 4, 1943
Sixth Award	Army-Navy E	Sept. 4, 1943
Seventh Award	Army-Navy E	Mar. 13, 1945
Original Award	Maritime M	Mar. 10, 1943
Second Award	Maritime M	May 3, 1944
Third Award	Maritime M	Oct. 18, 1944
Fourth Award	Maritime M	Mar. 27, 1945

EVERETT SUPERCHARGER DIVISION

Original Award	Army-Navy E	Apr. 10, 1943
Second Award	Army-Navy E	Jan. 6, 1945
Third Award	Army-Navy E	July 28, 1945

FITCHBURG PLANT

Original Award	Army-Navy E	Nov. 18, 1944
Second Award	Army-Navy E	Apr. 30, 1945
Original Award	Maritime M	Mar. 31, 1945

FORT EDWARD PLANT

Original Award	Army-Navy E	May 10, 1945

FORT WAYNE WORKS

Original Award	Navy E	May 20, 1942
Second Award	Army-Navy E	May 22, 1943
Third Award	Army-Navy E	Feb. 7, 1944

ONTARIO WORKS

Original Award	Army-Navy E	Dec. 12, 1942
Second Award	Army-Navy E	July 17, 1943
Third Award	Army-Navy E	Mar. 4, 1944
Fourth Award	Army-Navy E	Oct. 21, 1944
Fifth Award	Army-Navy E	May 26, 1945

PHILADELPHIA WORKS

Original Award	Navy E	May 20, 1942
Second Award	Army-Navy E	Nov. 15, 1942
Third Award	Army-Navy E	May 15, 1943
Fourth Award	Army-Navy E	Dec. 10, 1943
Fifth Award	Army-Navy E	June 14, 1944
Sixth Award	Army-Navy E	May 25, 1945

PITTSFIELD WORKS

Original Award	Army-Navy E	July 18, 1943
Second Award	Army-Navy E	July 22, 1943
Third Award	Army-Navy E	Jan. 21, 1944
Fourth Award	Army-Navy E	July 28, 1944

Plastics Division

Original Award	Army-Navy E	July 23, 1943
Second Award	Army-Navy E	Jan. 8, 1944
Third Award	Army-Navy E	July 22, 1944

River Works

Original Award	Navy E	May 29, 1942
Second Award	Army-Navy E	Dec. 16, 1942
Third Award	Army-Navy E	May 15, 1943
Fourth Award	Army-Navy E	Dec. 10, 1943
Fifth Award	Army-Navy E	July 5, 1944
Sixth Award	Army-Navy E	June 9, 1945
Original Award	Maritime M	July 5, 1944
Second Award	Maritime M	Oct. 26, 1944

Schenectady Works

Original Award	Navy E	May 23, 1942
Second Award	Army-Navy E	Sept. 14, 1942
Third Award	Army-Navy E	Feb. 7, 1944
Fourth Award	Army-Navy E	Apr. 30, 1945

Syracuse Plant

| Original Award | Army-Navy E | June 24, 1943 |

Trenton Plant

| Original Award | Army-Navy E | Jan. 2, 1945 |

West Lynn Works

Original Award	Navy E	June 19, 1942
Second Award	Army-Navy E	Dec. 16, 1942
Third Award	Army-Navy E	May 22, 1943
Fourth Award	Army-Navy E	Dec. 10, 1943
Fifth Award	Army-Navy E	June 9, 1945

York Plant

Original Award	Army-Navy E	July 29, 1943
Second Award	Army-Navy E	Jan. 26, 1944
Third Award	Army-Navy E	July 20, 1944
Fourth Award	Army-Navy E	Feb. 7, 1945

Affiliated Companies

CARBOLOY COMPANY, INC.

Original Award	Army-Navy E	Sept. 24, 1943
Second Award	Army-Navy E	June 23, 1945

EDISON GENERAL ELECTRIC APPLIANCE COMPANY

Original Award	Army-Navy E	Feb. 27, 1943
Second Award	Army-Navy E	Dec. 31, 1943
Third Award	Army-Navy E	July 22, 1944
Fourth Award	Army-Navy E	Mar. 10, 1945

GENERAL ELECTRIC X-RAY CORPORATION

Original Award	Army-Navy E	Jan. 23, 1943
Second Award	Army-Navy E	July 17, 1943
Third Award	Army-Navy E	Mar. 11, 1944

Index